A DAMSEL IN DISTRESS
Part One

Compiled by

Janice Hylton-Thompson

Published by

Anointed Scribes Publishing

Newark, New Jersey

The Naked Wife

A Damsel in Distress

Your Voice, Her Voice, My Voice,

One Voice, Our Voice

ISBN 978-1-946242-07-5

P.O. Box 9881
Newark NJ 07104

Thank You

Words cannot express my gratitude to the countless wives and women who have opened up to me and trusted me to tell your stories. I call you "My Sistas." You Sistas, had me crying, laughing, sitting on the edge of my seat, getting mad, angry and upset all at the same time. I almost jumped on a few planes to come and rescue a few of you precious Sistas!!

I'm sure I've gotten a few wrinkles from the frowns on my face and the popping and bulging eyes from your stories. Thank you, Sistas, for your patience, for every time I called, texted, emailed or Facebook you for clarification on your accounts. I thank you for your grace, patience, love and your encouragement to finally get it done.

Six years, later, I am so honored and blessed to be the vessel that you choose to give your stories a voice. Your voice, her voice, my voice, our voice, one voice. I pray the BLESSING over your life! I pray for your strength in the Lord. I pray that God will grant you the desires of your hearts and that your joy might be full.

I want to remind you of how special you are to God. Every tear you cry is bottled up by the Lord. The Lord has numbered every hair on your head. There is nowhere you can go that God your father, can't find you. God loves you so much that he gave his only begotten son Jesus, to die for you. That means you are unique and He loves you with an everlasting love!!

God is the breasted one, and he awaits your presence to spend time with you. Remember that you are a Princess, the daughter of the King, and God wants you to walk in your royalty and your authority that he has graced you with. Thank you again!! And I love every one of you!!

Thank You

Many supporters have helped me to get THE NAKED WIFE completed. And for that, I will forever be grateful. Thank you, and God bless you!

However, I want to take a few seconds to thank a few loved ones:

Bishop Marvin Bradshaw & First Lady Edna Bradshaw: S.I.G.H. . . . .

Only in heaven, you will know the impact that you have had on my life. I just cannot put in words how much of a blessing you have been to me over these last 23 years!!

When I came to Faith Christian Center, I was just a seventeen-year-old homeless teen mom, with a baby. As a forty-year-old woman, those years in FCC and the lessons you've taught me have kept me and will continue to keep me until the end of my journey here on earth!!

I humbly bow down and take my shoes off to you both
Love and appreciate you much!!

Mr. Wonderful-Michael:

Thank you for being a wonderful husband who continues to profess your love for me, provide a comfortable home for the children and I and for protecting us.

Thank you for always supporting my dream, gift, and talent. Thank you for pushing me to be the great author you always tell me that I am. Thank you for the many days and nights that you blessed me to work on my writing projects. Thank you for always making my favorite meal to keep me going!! LOL!! I could not have accomplished any of this without your love and continual support. I LLLLOOOOOOOOOOO YOU!!! LOL!!

Denice Scholar:

I call you my Sista from another mother!!! You have been such an inspiration and a great friend to me. Thank you for your many words of love, support, and encouragement. Thank you for a assisting me in so many ventures and always being there when I want to whine. LOL!!! My life is so much better because of you, doll!! Love you!!

Melanie Liebhart Sadler:

Gurly, what would I have done without you with this project!? You have been such a huge help during this journey. You have been like Grace and Mercy, always there to help, hold up my hand like Aaron did Moses. Thank you for always being there for me. Love you doll!!

MAFS:

And finally, all of my Lovers @ MAFS. I call it my haven and you guys my angels. Whenever I feel beaten up, I can always run there to get a word of encouragement or laugh.

To my many supporters, who support and always ask for the next book, I am because of you!! Thank you!!

Dedication

I dedicate THE NAKED WIFE to every woman and wife! But, especially to my Sistas, who are single and desire to get married. Your sisters in THE NAKED WIFE, shared their stories, not only so that their voices could be heard, but so that you "our" sisters would read their stories and learn from them.

Please pay attention to red flags and warning signs. Choose better husbands and know your worth. Stick to your standards. Do not compromise who you are just to say you have a man.

Most importantly, if you don't have a father figure in your life, I encourage you to find one. Perhaps your pastor, uncle, an older co-worker or someone that can talk to you like a father will to his daughter. My spiritual father Bishop Marvin Bradshaw Sr. saved me from so many mistakes as a young single woman. And for that, I will forever be grateful!!

Finally, please share this book with another sister. I often say, Sisters Saving Sisters! And as you move from Single Women 2 Married Women – Wise Up (My Facebook group for women) I encourage you to wise up. Dating is a game, and it's essential to learn the rules.

Many single women are playing the game, without knowing the rules. But not you!! When you are finished reading this book, you will be wiser and well equipped to recognize the game and apply the rules. As one sister said "I think we as women marry stupidly, and I think we need to teach our daughters not to do that. And THE NAKED WIFE, I think is going to do that."

The Word of the Lord

Genesis 3:6-7; 21

[6] And when the woman saw that the tree was good for food and that it was pleasant to the eyes, and a tree to be desired to make one wise, she took of the fruit thereof, and did eat, and also gave unto her husband with her; and he did eat. [7] And the eyes of them both were opened, and they knew that they were naked, and they sewed fig leaves together, and made themselves aprons.

[8] And they heard the voice of the LORD God walking in the garden in the cool of the day: and Adam and his wife hid themselves from the presence of the LORD God amongst the trees of the garden. [9] And the LORD God called unto Adam, and said unto him, Where art thou? [10] And he said, I heard thy voice in the garden, and I was afraid, because I was naked; and I hid myself.

[11] And he said, Who told thee that thou wast naked? Hast thou eaten of the tree, whereof I commanded thee that thou shouldest not eat? [12] And the man said, The woman whom thou gavest to be with me, she gave me of the tree, and I did eat. [13] And the LORD God said unto the woman, What is this that thou hast done? And the woman said, The serpent beguiled me, and I did eat.

[21] Unto Adam also and to his wife did the LORD God make coats of skins, and clothed them.

Ezekiel 16:8

Now when I passed by thee, and looked upon thee, behold, thy time was the time of love; and I spread my skirt over thee, and covered thy nakedness: yea, I sware unto thee, and entered into a covenant with thee, saith the Lord GOD, and thou becamest mine.

Table of Contents

Introduction

*O*ver the years, many women have asked me to write something for women who want to get married. And for wives who were going through a tough time in their marriages. But honestly, I had nothing at that point because I was still single. Therefore, I wasn't able to share anything from a personal standpoint.

The more I wrote on other subjects, the more the requests came in to write something for women and wives. But, the Lord had not given me a revelation on that topic. You see, I have been writing for over twenty years, and unless the Lord gives me something specific, I just can't write about a subject.

Nevertheless, I gave my word that I would continually ask the Lord about what to write. Over time, when I interacted with various women via different venues, which includes events for my other books, *(Praying for Our Children, In Christ I Am…, Moments of Gratitude)*, I was heartbroken by the number of wives that were going through a tough time in their marriages. I was also puzzled by the number of wives who were still dealing with situations that their relationships had struggled with while courting and being engaged.

Additionally, I was shocked that a lot of the issues that wives were experiencing were issues that were fixable. However, their husbands had no interest in working on their marriages. Neither were they willing to take a simple step like marriage counseling to save their marriages.

Over time, the cries of wives who were going through divorces, separations, infidelities of their husbands, abuse, financial burden, foreclosure, sexual abuse of their children, abandonment, and ill-treatment caused me to pause! There were even 'Christian' wives who were divorced, and their husbands were married to other women. But, they believed, God would guide their ex-husbands to divorce their new wives and come back to them.

I always remember the advice I received in premarital counseling. Our counselor said, "Both of you need to be committed to the marriage for it to work." I understood that as meaning there is a cause and effect. To have a happy and fulfilling marriage where we both can benefit, it will take both of us working together to make the marriage work.

Additionally, I understood the counselor's statement to mean that both of us needed to be committed and submit to God first and then to each other. Both of us had to be giving of ourselves, sacrificing, readjusting, realigning, and listening to each other. Both needed to be faithful, thoughtful, caring and giving for our marriage to work.

However, the flipside to that is if we both do not work towards the marriage, it will not work.

And that is why it is essential for all women to make sure that the men you are preparing to marry are willing to make the marriage work. That means there will be some adjustments and changes that need to occur to make room in your lives for each other.

Single ladies, it is crucial, that you are not unequally yoked with the men you are planning to marry. If you get yoked up with the wrong man, you will end up carrying most, if not all, of the responsibilities of the marriage. Additionally, you will eventually die under the pressure of the burden, because your yoke is uneven, and your marriage is lopsided.

It is necessary for every woman planning to marry your potential husband that you pay attention to the RED FLAGS. Red flags are like warning signs. If you do not take heed, then you might (God forbid) end up having an accident, and only God knows what the result will be.

So, I know you love him, ladies, but he hasn't worked in 10 years!? Question, why are you planning on marrying him? Do you understand that God created the husband to provide for his wife and family?

Are you willing to take care of and provide for him for the rest of his life? Or has he told you that once you get married, he is going to get a job? Perhaps you think that once you are married, you can influence him to get a job? Why marry him when he is not working and expect him to change when you get married? *GURL, THAT'S A RED FLAG!!*

If you are a Naked Wife, I pray that you will see yourself thoroughly in this book. I encourage you to use this opportunity to reinvent yourself and realize that you are worth more than you understand. And if you allow the Lord, he will take you to higher heights and deeper depths of his love for you.

I pray that as all women read *The Naked Wife*, that you will be blessed with the answers and wisdom that you seek. May the Lord guide you in the decisions that you will make.

JANICE HYLTON-THOMPSON

The Naked Wife

*M*any have asked me how I came up with the title of *The Naked Wife*. The truth is, I didn't come up with the title at all! But, it was a revelation from the Lord. As I met various women, especially in the Church, I discovered that there were many "silent sufferers" disguised as happy wives. With this, I began to talk to the Lord about a word of encouragement for wives and women. "Lord, give it to me, Jesus!" I would often pray in my time of prayer and scripture reading.

One day, as I was going about my daily activities, the Lord said, *"The Naked Wife!"*

"Now, Lord, what kind of freaky stuff is that? Do you want me to write one of those scandalous books? You know I've always wanted to write one!" I giggled!

"No, no!" said the Lord. "When a husband does not do what he was created, called, anointed, destined, and appointed to do, he leaves his wife feeling NAKED! After all, a husband is a call!"

Yall, if I could have fainted, I would have! That is such a revelation and an eye-opener! It was as if the light came on for me in my own life and in the stories, women would often share with me. It was then the cries of many women and wives made sense! *THANK YOU, JESUS!*

One day, I spoke to a very close friend and sister whose husband had been unfaithful throughout their five years of marriage. He refused to go to counseling and address his issues. She desperately wanted to save the marriage for her children's sake, but he had no interest in preserving it.

As we talked, she said, "I just don't understand why he got married and then turned around and treated me this way! He just makes me feel so…"

"NAKED?" I completed her sentence.

"Yes, that's it. I feel NAKED!" She whispered.

5

As I wiped away the tears that ran down her cheeks, I shook my head and said, *"THE NAKED WIFE!"*

"NAKED" is not sexy or sexual. But, it is a NAKEDNESS of a wife of not being covered by her husband. A NAKEDNESS of not being loved, valued, protected, and provided for by her husband. It is NAKEDNESS of a wife taking on a husband's responsibility that he vowed to do for her and their children.

It is about the NAKEDNESS of taking on roles that God did not create a wife to do. Instead of being provided for, she's the provider. Instead of being protected, she is the protector. Instead of her husband fighting to save their marriage, she is the one that is fighting. Instead of flourishing in a safe environment provided by her husband so that she can nurture him and their children, it is one of tension, stress, and danger!

Instead of being loved and cherished by the passion and attention of her husband, she is left feeling NAKED because of his extramarital affairs. Those same hands he used to place a ring on her finger while they stood before God, the pastor, family and friends, he now uses them to beat her. She must now become aggressive to defend herself and her children.

When a husband doesn't take the time out of his busy day to call or send a text to say I love you, miss you, and I am thinking of you, it leaves her feeling NAKED! When a husband is too busy to appreciate his wife, it leaves her feeling NAKED.

You see, it is a husband's responsibility to provide for every need that his wife has. The provision and protection of a husband for his wife and his children is like that of parents for their child. It is the parent's responsibility to make sure that they provide for every need that the child has. The child should not have to go outside of his parents to get any need met.

So, it is when it comes to marriage. God's intention for a husband and wife is that he provides for his wife in the areas that God created him to provide for. When a husband doesn't do that, it leaves his wife not only feeling NAKED but being NAKED!

The First Marriage

*T*he story of Adam and Eve is one that has fascinated me as a student of the Bible, and I always come back to it. I felt as if something just wasn't right about the story and Eve was unfairly blamed for the fall of man. I had never actually studied the story in depth, but there was always a feeling of unease when I read it. As I completed *The Naked Wife*, I wanted to take another look at the story of Adam and Eve, again.

God formed Adam with Eve already in him. And, when Adam was ready and able to provide, protect, and speak to and for her, God brought Eve out of him. When God brought Eve to Adam, what did Adam do? He told her who she is.

Adam said you are woman in Genesis 2:21-25, **And the rib, which the LORD God had taken from man, made he a woman and brought her unto the man.**

[23] And Adam said, This is now bone of my bones, and flesh of my flesh: she shall be called Woman, because she was taken out of Man.

[24] Therefore shall a man leave his father and his mother, and shall cleave unto his wife: and they shall be one flesh.

[25] And they were both naked, the man and his wife, and were not ashamed.

Notice, Eve didn't come to an unprepared man, a man who only had potential, a man who couldn't provide for her or put a shelter over her head. When Eve met Adam, he was a complete man who was able to profess, provide, and protect her. Eve was in need of nothing! He was not half of a man; he was not a man trying to find a job or trying to put food on the table. He was able to provide for her every need.

God never told Eve to build Adam, nor to tell him who he was. God gave Adam a vision and a purpose and then told him to tell Eve who she was. So, all the brothers that are walking around saying they need a woman who can build them up and marry them because they have potential, wait a minute! Let's go back to the Bible and read it! Eve did not have to build Adam up to be the man she needed him to be so that he could turn around and be her husband so that he could provide and protect her.

Man is the only species that births something (woman), and then turns around and tells her to, "protect, provide, clothe, and tend to my needs." *"I want you to go out there work your fingers to the bone, bring home the bacon, cook it and feed it to me, make me burp, and put me to sleep."* What is wrong with that picture?

God gave Adam the Word, and he was to teach Eve what God said! This also speaks of the husband being the watchman on the wall for his family and him to teach his family. Adam was to profess, provide, protect, shield, care for, and teach Eve. That is why when Eve ate the fruit, nothing happened. But when the head — the protector, provider, and professor-ate it, everything changed.

Please be informed, that the enemy wants to take the head, protector, watchman, provider out of his God-ordained place of power and authority. When the head is not in effect, his purpose becomes vulnerable. That is why it is vital for the man to be in his rightful place so that he can make sure his wife and children are safe, provided for, and protected.

Question: If Adam was supposed to do all of this for his wife, how in God's name did Eve have time to entertain Satan aka another man? How is it that Eve was able to believe another man's voice over that of her professor, protector, and provider? How is it that Eve was out trying to find food for them?

You can read more in my book *The Sacrifice of Marriage*, coming soon.

Christ and the Church

The marriage of Adam and Eve is our first example of marriage. However, Adam and Eve, in my opinion, messed up big time. Therefore, Christ decided to come and show us how it is supposed to be done. Like Adam who had Eve inside of him, Christ also had the Church in Him. And, in due time He gave birth to her. Jesus encourages husbands in Ephesians to love their wives like He loves the Church. What did Christ do for the Church? He died for her!

Christ never asked the Church to tell Him who He is. He already knows who He is. He said I am the Alpha and the Omega, the beginning and the end. He never told the Church to die for Him based on a potential. No, He said, "Because I give my life for you, follow me!" Jesus understood that marriage is a sacrifice.

Christ tells the Church who she is. He said, "You are bought with a price. You are a royal priesthood, a peculiar people." He told us that we are seated with Him in heavenly places. Christ is the builder, provider, protector, and He professes His love to the Church.

The Church, in turn, worships, praises, and honors Christ, and rehearses to Him who He is. It is not for His sake, it is for ours, but it makes Him feel good and puts a smile on His face, knowing that His woman is secure in knowing that HE IS THE MAN!

That is why it is crucial for us to know who we are. Our purpose and the reason God created us. You can read more in my book series, *In Christ I Am...*

When Adam caused them to come out from under God's umbrella of protection and provision, what happened? They became NAKED. And what did they do? They tried to find and provide for themselves by sewing fig leaves together to cover their NAKEDNESS! And what did God do? He had to make a sacrifice to cover them. Husbands, covering your wife is a sacrifice! Fulfilling your God-ordained, anointed purpose of providing, protecting, and professing is a sacrifice.

Who Are You?

*W*hile compiling *The Naked Wife,* one of the things I noticed couples struggling with is their roles. I think we need to have a basic understanding of who we are and the functions which God has assigned us to fulfill.

<u>Women/Wives</u> were not created by God to be providers. Think on that. Unfortunately, because of circumstances, we become providers because we have to. If we have children, we have to provide for ourselves and our children. But, in God's eternal plan, He did not create us to be providers.

Men/Husbands were created by God to be providers. Some husbands are not providers but look to their wives to provide for them. In God's eternal plan, He did not create wives to be the providers for their husbands or their families!

So, ladies, if you are getting ready to marry a man and he is not able to provide for you at least at the level you are used to providing for yourself and your children, then you might want to re-think that.

Wives were created by God to be nurturers! Therefore, when wives are busy being providers and having to deal with the stress and burden of providing; we are not able to entirely be who God created us to be — nurturers of our husbands and children.

As wives, our focus should be our husbands and children, and not on stressing over how we are going to pay the next bill and how we are going to meet this month's expenses? So, am I saying that women shouldn't work? Nope, that's not what I said. I said a wife's focus should be her husband and her children. Wives should not stress over the bills. God did not create us for that! Personally, I believe that if a wife works, it needs to be by choice and not out of necessity to pay bills.

Someone might say, "I don't worry or stress because I trust God!" If you are a wife with a husband in the house, you should not have to go to God about paying your rent, putting food on the table, and clothes on your back. That's like us going to another man asking him to help us to pay our rent. He is going to ask you, "Well, aren't you married?"

Just ask Eve! People always want to blame her for talking to the devil, but what woman who is happy at home has time to entertain another man? What woman who trusts the voice of her husband believes another man's voice over that of her husband?

I am not saying Eve was right; she was wrong. However, a husband needs to understand that when he leaves his wife naked, she will look for cover somewhere else. When the husband is not rehearsing the Word of the Lord to his wife and spending time talking and connecting with her, it leaves space for the voice of another to slither in. Husbands, you are your wives' protectors, providers, and prophets.

It is a husband's charge by God to provide a safe, happy, fulfilling, and protected environment where his wife can flourish. So that she can walk in the purpose that God created her to walk in, to nurture her husband and their children. So, husbands, if you come home to a house of stress, strife, and contention, check that! Ask yourself, "Have I provided an environment where my wife can nurture me?"

When Adam sinned and disobeyed God's Word, what happened? Because of Adam's actions, they became naked, hid, and sewed fig leaves to cover themselves. Do you know why they sinned? (And note that it was not sin until Adam ate the fruit.) Because Adam was not rehearsing God's Word, and he wasn't teaching Eve. Every action of a husband causes a reaction!

Deuteronomy says — Teach, rehearse, hang God's Word on your doorposts, etc. When they sinned, they tried to fix it. Likewise, is the case with some wives. When their husbands don't do what they were created, appointed, anointed, and destined to do, the wives become naked and then try to fix it, and seek to find cover elsewhere.

God had clothed them in His glory, but when Adam caused them to come out from God's covering, they were walking around in fig leaves. How many wives are walking around naked, trying to fix it, covered in fig leaves versus being covered by the glory, protection, and provisions of her husband?

And God, in His love and grace, had to make a sacrifice to clothe them. Marriage is a sacrifice, loved ones!

The above excerpt is from my book, *The Sacrifice of Marriage,* coming soon.

An Eye-Opener

I must admit that compiling this book has been an eye-opener for me. When reading some of the stories, I was honestly shocked! I couldn't fathom that adults could act and behave in such a manner.

In my thinking, when we get married we understand the vows, and we are to act accordingly. However, some wives found themselves in marriages that were not the intention of God the Father when He created marriage and did not exemplify the marriage between Christ and the Church.

These are stories of abuse, abandonment, infidelity, financial burdens, fraud, perpetrated by the husbands who vowed to love, honor, and protect their wives but did the opposite. Many of these stories are from the Saints, who are expected to be examples to everyone else.

In the meantime, there are some stories of wives who have vowed to stick with it at any cost. Some wives say, "So what if he's cheating, I'm not going anywhere!" That is their right.

The Naked Wife is not to bash husbands or marriage. Marriage was created by God to be beautiful, fulfilling, and happy, and is an example of the relationship between Christ and the Church. In the meantime, like our walk with Christ, there are many trials, tests, and tribulations. However, if each person is committed to the marriage, it will work.

Perhaps the rest of us can learn from it by submitting to each other. Additionally, this is an opportunity for us to have some honest conversations about what is going on in our own lives, to see what, if anything, we can do to get back under the covering of Christ.

The Naked Wife is an anthology of stories and testimonies shared by over two hundred women. There is something in here for everyone, and there might be a few stories that make you think, "I'm going through this, too." Perhaps, this book can save your marriage if you both are willing to work on it by having a 'come to Jesus moment.'

Everyone can glean something out of *The Naked Wife*. I encourage you to have some of these conversations honestly with your friends and husbands.

I especially encourage singles to read this book, because it will help you to identify some red flags that you might have been ignoring. *The Naked Wife* will help you to seek more answers or even say goodbye. I can indeed say I understand why God gave me this title *THE NAKED WIFE!*

Singles

*P*lease allow me space and grace, to speak a word to my single Ladies who desire to get married. I add *"who desire to get married"*, because every woman does not want to get married. When you desire to get married, your lifestyle must be one of a "wife." Because you desire to get married, you will carry yourself differently and your lifestyle will be one of precision and discipline.

You can't be like and live your life, like your single friends who does not want to be married and who feel as if they don't need a husband.

I am here to tell you that a husband is a need!!

If your single girlfriends live their lives like a hotel, where everyone comes in and out, you can't be like that! Why? Because you are a wife!! The wife of a good man and husband. Therefore, you must live your life as if you are his wife.

You will never have to think that I, Janice Hylton-Thompson, don't understand the struggles of a single woman who wants to get married. Trust me I do and always will. I got married when I was thirty-five. That is "OLD" in marriage and baby land!! Lol!! So, please be encouraged!!

Singles, here's something I would like for you to keep in mind as you read *The Naked Wife*. Next to your decision for Christ; which is the most critical decision of your life, the next most important decision is the man whom you choose to marry. I will go more in depth in my book for singles, but as you read *The Naked Wife*, I ask you to keep that thought in mind.

I pray that every single and engaged woman reads *The Naked Wife*. One of the questions I asked my Naked Wives was: did they see any red flags with their husbands when they were dating or engaged?

About 85-90% of my Naked Wives admitted to seeing red flags and things that they were uncomfortable with. However, they hoped that once they were married that the men would change and become the husbands they needed.

Now, in all fairness none of us is perfect, and we are all works in progress. However, there needs to be a progression to being better men and women and working on or towards those things we need to work on.

Potential

Many of the wives stated that they were encouraged as young women that if a man had potential to give him a "chance." As a young woman, I was encouraged to do the same also. However, I always wondered, why would I take a chance with my life and that of my daughter's?

Unfortunately, many women took the advice but, their little boy husbands never grew up to be mature men! And many wives, ten years later still had "potential" for a husband. Ladies, potential can be a very tricky thing, so let's look at some examples.

Ladies, there is a difference between a man that's going back to school to better himself vs. a man that's been talking about going back to school for the last ten years.

There's a difference between a man that works at a fast-food restaurant and is satisfied vs. a man that's working at the fast-food restaurant and working to own it.

There's a difference between a man that works for someone at a mechanic shop vs. a man that's working and building to own his own. If you must tell him he can own his own and you have to do the work, then for the entirety of the relationship, you will be like his Momma!

However, as wives, we are to encourage and support our husband's dreams and visions. When God brought Eve to Adam, he was already working his dream and vision!

And that's apart of submission ladies. You are to submit to your husband's vision. But, if he doesn't have a vision, what exactly are you submitting to? You can read more in my upcoming book-*The Sacrifice of Marriage*.

My Sistas, there's a difference between a man that is paying his child support vs. a man you must make pay his child support. If you have to tell him to pay his child support, leave him alone.

There is a difference between a man that has a relationship with Jesus, vs. a man you have to coerce or tease into going to church. Ladies, there's a difference between a man who has a gift or talent and working on it and working at the same time to provide vs. a man that's just working on his craft but can't feed or provide for his family. Because in the meantime you have to eat! Leave forty, and fifty-year-old wanna be rappers alone; who want to live off you vs. working his craft and working to take care of you at the same time.

Ladies, if there is a man that you are interested in and he has "potential" pay close attention. What is he doing about his potential? And in the meantime, what is he doing to provide for himself? If you marry him, can he provide for you with what he have going?

Please do not say that you will take care of him with your income until he "makes it!" Please stop taking care of grown men who are looking for a handout!

Can someone please explain to me how some women get with a man that you have to provide for? He comes to you empty handed with neither a pot to pee in or a window to throw it through, but you are glad to take him and take care of him!?

PLEASE UNDERSTAND AND GET IT IN YOUR HEAD AND HEART THAT A HUSBAND IS TO:

1. PROFESS HIS LOVE TO AND FOR YOU
2. PROVIDE FOR YOU (He is to show your father or you that he can provide for you better than you were providing for yourself!)
3. PROTECT YOU!

AND LADIES FOR GOD'S SAKE, YES THAT INCLUDES HIM PROTECTING YOU WITH HIS MONEY!!!

So, please stop this bull crap that you don't need his money!!

YES, YOU DO!!!

Pay attention to all of the success stories. Successful people were working towards perfecting their craft, but at the same time, they were providing for their wives and children.

Red Flags

Some wives admitted that they knew their boyfriends or fiancé were cheating but hoped that once they got married that he would change.

(Insert......B.L.A.N.K....S.T.A.R.E.S....here.)

Question: After how many chances will you give him to cheat and stop? When is he expected to be faithful to you? But many women marry men that they know are cheating or who is a woman beater!!

People often ask if a man cheats, does that mean he will cheat forever? If he hit you once, does that mean he will hit you again? I can't answer those questions with certainty, but I know one thing: You are who you are!

- Cheaters Cheat
- Abusers Abuse
- Liars Lie And
- Thieves Steal

One young lady who is currently going through a divorce after five years of marriage counseling, the story was unfortunate. She said after waiting years to meet her "Boaz" that she finally met a nice man. At first, she wasn't attracted to him but decided to go out with him.

After some time, he was talking marriage, but she was uncomfortable with his age, stubbornness, procrastination, lack of communication, cheating and a host of other issues. She said, one day she was talking to her older friend about him and how uncomfortable she was with him.

Then she said, "you know what, I'm just gonna go ahead and marry him because I haven't met anyone else." How sad is this!!??

(Insert......SHOCKED FACE....here.)

Throughout the planning of the wedding, it was all on her, and she was the one dragging him to counseling. When she talked to him about it, he insisted that he would change. The only issue with that was he showed no signs of improving.

And it wasn't long after they got married that they began to have significant issues with all the things she was uncomfortable with along with him being unfaithful and physically abusive. You see in marriage, both need to readjust, realign and work together to make the marriage work.

So, you see my Sistas; it's critical not to ignore red flags, hoping that he will change. Sure, none of us is perfect, but if the person's actions don't line up to what they are saying, then take their actions over their words!

Did You Know?

Ok, you see the fairy tale, the dress, and all the celebrations that come with being married. But do you realize that when you get married; *YOU ARE TURNING YOUR LIFE OVER TO YOUR HUSBAND?* Yes, it is an exchange that takes place at the altar.

When you get married, your husband will be your power of attorney and you his. You are turning everything about you over to this man. He is to profess his love, provide for and protect you. He will now speak for you, make decisions for you and every action he makes will affect you! Therefore, it is imperative that you choose the right husband because your life and destiny depend on the man that you choose.

Something I did when I was dating, was once there was mutual interest, I removed my heart from the process. See, your heart will cause you to overlook red flags and be compassionate to a man who needs your help, vs. choosing a good man with husband qualities. However, your mind will honestly think about those red flags. Look at the pros and cons. And of course, I always got my spiritual father involved.

Be Honest!

Question: Can the man that you are about to TURN YOUR LIFE OVER TO, profess his love for you and only you? Can he provide better for you than you were yourself and protect you? Can you honestly trust this man with your life? Your heart, your child, your finances, your bank account, your protection, and provision?

19

Can you trust the decisions he will make for you? Can you trust that he will take care of you or does he need your help to take care of you? Can he speak for you or do you have to do all the talking for you both?

Ladies, this was something else I lived by when I was dating. I believe a woman needs to be comfortable living at the level her husband can provide. Not what he will be able to provide later when things get better, but where he is now. I also believe that we need to love and marry the man in front of us. Not who he is going to be, but instead love and marry the man who is right in front of you.

Therefore, if he only makes $25,000 per year, can you be comfortable living on his income or do you need to add yours to be comfortable? If you won't be satisfied living on his income ALONE, don't marry him!!

I honestly believe, that if women who are dating to get married, be honest about this one issue, the divorce rate would be cut by 50%. It puzzles me when a wife says her husband works here and there and he does the best he can!? EXCUSE ME??? That sound like my brothers when they were teenagers trying to find summer jobs as teens!? LOL!!

The issue with us women these days is that we have switched roles! Many women have taken on a man's roles and responsibility, and the men have taken on women's roles. The women are the ones doing the professing, protecting and the providing!! *PLEASE STOP IT, LADIES!!!*

You are worth covering by the man you are about to marry and yes, that includes covering you with his ability to provide for you!

You cover him in your prayers!

My motto when I was dating was that "I would prefer to be single and happy than to be married and miserable!" Ladies, I know so many unhappy married and naked wives!! All because they ignored the red flags. You don't believe me? Read the rest of *The Naked Wife.*

One young wife asked, "why didn't God tell me not to marry him?" I then asked about any red flags or signs that she had seen while dating and she listed several in a matter of seconds. I then let her know that even though God didn't speak in an audible voice, those signs were Him talking to her.

The Daddy Card

My Sistas, I urge you not ignore the red flags because that's God speaking to you. Another thing I did, was to take a man that was talking marriage to talk to my Pastor and spiritual father, Bishop Bradshaw. You see, the same way as women we know another woman is the same way men know another man. Plus, it's important to show that you have a father or male figure in your life that does love and adore you and is protecting you.

Additionally, if there were a guy that I wasn't sure about, I would say "you know what, I want you to meet my dad!" And guess what? They would disappear. You see their motives were not right and I played the daddy card that will chase vultures away. When a guy had the guts to meet my dad, he would ask "so, what is your intentions to my daughter and my granddaughter?"

The Cookie

I'm so tired of seeing my sistas cry on social media that they dated a guy for two or three months, he wined and dined them, and as soon as he got the 'cookie' he was "ghost!" My answer for that is: *"Stop Dishing Out the Cookie!!"*

Do you understand how important your vagina is?? How do you just give it to any and every man that shows interest in "you?" Your vagina is your holy of holies, created for your husband ONLY!! Ok, sure, we've all given up the cookie sometime or the other! I had my baby when I was 16 years old, and I was not a virgin when I got married. But the question is:" When do we make that turn and change?"

You've heard the saying "the meaning of insanity is doing the same thing over and over, but expecting a change." In other words, to have what you never had, you must do what you have never done!!

TAKE THE COOKIE OFF THE TABLE!!

So, ladies, of course, the guy you thought was "it" has "ghost" you once you gave up the cookie because his goal was to get the cookie!! But, you were so caught up in your emotions, that you were not paying attention to the "game!"

21

Ladies, men were created to CONQUER!! So, some men are going around looking to conquer as many women as possible!! Think about it this way, as my daddy used to say *EVERY MAN WANTS TO HAVE SEX!!* And every man that approaches you has an agenda. It is either to conquer you or make you his wife!! So, ladies:

TAKE THE COOKIE OFF THE TABLE!! AIN'T NOBODY GETTING ANY COOKIES!!

You see ladies, by *TAKING THE COOKIE OF THE TABLE,* that will save you 95% of your time, energy, many broken hearts and possible babies out of wedlock. And can you say possibly *SEXUALLY TRANSMITTED DISEASES!?* So, once they realize that you're not giving up the cookie, they won't want to "waste" their time, because their agenda was to *GET THE COOKIE!!*

But wait a minute!! Remember that this is a *"GAME!"* So, there might be a few that will stick around because they are determined! So, play the daddy card ladies.

And, when all else fails, think of your future husband! Before I got married, there were men that I worked with who told me that they heard that I wasn't giving up the cookie to anyone. But that they were going to get "it"!! I just laughed at them!! Well, I am honored to say, not one of them got my cookie!!! And guess what, those same men shake my husband's hand when we have events. So, I hold my head high, because my husband doesn't have to be ashamed!!

Also, please do not put yourself in compromising positions! He doesn't need to come to your house and for God sakes, stop going to men's house for a first date to watch movies!! If he is inviting you over to his home to watch a movie, he doesn't value you, and his goal is to *GET THE COOKIE!!*

Standards

What are your standards? What do you want in a husband? Can you list ten things that you want in a husband both negotiable and non-negotiables? Ladies, have you ever thought that you continue to fall victim to vultures because you don't have a clear understanding of what you want in a husband? Because there is a difference between vultures and eagles! They both fly but, their purposes are different! You have ten fingers, write them on your fingers and stick to it. Therefore, when a fake approach you, you can identify him immediately.

Counterfeits

I heard a story about how bankers identify fake money. You would think they study the fake ones, right? Nope, as the story goes, they spend so much time studying the real money, that when a counterfeit comes across their eyes and hands, they can identify it immediately.

That's how you must be with what you desire in a husband. Spend time in God's word about the ladies who got married and the husbands they chose. Put that together with what you want, your standards and stick to it. Now, ladies, please don't be so heavenly spiritual that you "ain't" no earthly good!! Use wisdom, please!! If a man scores at least a "7" of your 10, honestly ask yourself if you can live with it.

However, to me, those are negotiables. So, for example, on my list, I wanted a husband that was never married or had kids, but that was negotiable for me. So, If I met a man who had all my other things on my list but was previously married and had a child, then that's someone I would investigate a bit more.

Another example. Ladies, let's be real, we love a tall drink of water. Lol!! I did too. Ladies, does he have to be 6"5'? What if he scores a nine on your list, but he is 6 feet? LOL!!! Go ahead and have coffee with the brother and see what he's about.

The last example, you meet a nice man. He is the right height, he gives you the butterflies, he will go to church and everything, and you see yourself having some pretty babies with him. BUT, HE AIN'T GOT NO JOB!!! He can't keep a job, hasn't worked in ten years, doesn't like to work and isn't trying to find one.

See, this is where the "take your heart out of it," comes into play. Your heart will say "oh he needs my help, I can fix him up, do his resume for him, find him a job and drive him to the interview and I will get him to work." In the meantime, your mind is screaming "NO!!!"

23

Why? Your brain knows the truth!! Your brain has already downloaded everything he said, calculated it, gave it to you in 10 different versions. But he is pulling at your heartstrings, and you won't listen to anyone. Because your heart has you blinded with compassion vs. the facts that you know.

When I was single, I had my list. And if a guy that approached me didn't fit in it, I didn't waste my time. For example, I didn't entertain men that were not born-again Christians. I don't care how sweet and kind he was if he was not in submission to Christ, there was no need for us to have another conversation. Not even coffee!! And y'all know, I love a duncacinno!! LOL!!

My beautiful sisters, you my darling doves, need to get to that point!

Anyways ladies, my book for singles will be coming out soon!!

Life Happens

*B*ack to *The Naked Wife* now. Unfortunately, life doesn't always work out the way we planned or hoped. When you were preparing for your wedding, it was probably the happiest time in your life. But, sometimes, the marriage doesn't work out, and it is devastating.

One wife said, "When your marriage isn't working out, and divorce is pending, it's like an earthquake that disrupts and destroys many of the people and things that you love and hold dearest to you."

It has been said that going through a divorce is "like pulling one of your limbs from your body until it comes off."

I encourage you that when 'life happens,' take a second to breathe. Cry if you need to, see a counselor if necessary. Get up, dust yourself off, and go on in God. Life is worth living; you have one life to live, and you do not get to do this life over again. Therefore, live it in God and to the fullest of your ability. Remember that *LIFE'S WORTH LIVING!*

The Lord promised that He would wipe away every tear. Also, He said He would never leave or forsake you, and that He is the breasted one. So, Daughters of the KING of Kings, when the man who has vowed to love, protect, provide, and profess disappoints you, remember that you have a Father who will never leave or forsake you.

Late in the midnight hour, when that one little tear runs down your beautiful cheek, remember that God has promised that He will wipe it away. And when the pressures of your situation make your head hurt, remember that your Father is the breasted one, and He is waiting for you to come and lay your head on His heart so that you can hear the beat of His love for you. This will enable and strengthen you to get back in tune with Him.

The Naked Wife is a platform for women to tell their many stories: YOUR VOICE, HER VOICE, MY VOICE, OUR VOICE, ONE VOICE!!

Without judgment, rebuttal or "you should have, would have, could have," questions, or disgust.

So here you have it: The Naked Wife, A Damsel in Distress, The Anthology!

The Naked Wife

A DAMSEL IN DISTRESS

The Anthology

JANICE HYLTON-THOMPSON

First Ladies

30 Years

*W*hat is the secret to a happy and lasting marriage? I don't know if there is a secret. I did everything right. We got married when we were in our twenties, and we both had nothing except each other. He was in the military. You know, in those days a lot of our men went to the military. By God's grace and mercy, he came back home, safe and sound to our babies and me.

We struggled to make ends meet, but we always had food, shelter, clothing and a whole lot of love. He could play the keyboard. Honey, he was anointed! I would always tell him that he needed to be playing in the church. So he played here and there and that brought in a few extra dollars, and things were looking up.

Then, we both got saved and started going to church, and it was just wonderful. Eventually, he got called into the ministry and began to pastor this lovely little church, and it grew and grew until we had to move out of there into a bigger building. The more he preached and taught, the more the congregation grew.

Sometime later, we were able to buy our first home. God kept on blessing us and life was good, considering where we were coming from. Then he started traveling and preaching, and that was where problems began. By this time we had already been married for 25 years.

The women would come to the church, and it was just terrible the way they acted. There was this one that would come to every service and sit in the second row, and everyone knew what was going on. I would sit there and act like I was his biggest cheerleader when all that time I knew my husband was cheating on me!

Honestly, I was just shocked! My childhood sweetheart that I had stuck with, through thick and thin treated me that way. We ate rice and beans on many nights, and if we had one piece of chicken, we would give it to the kids, so they could have meat on their plate. When he wasn't working, I would scrub people's floors to make ends meet.

There were times when I went into the white neighborhoods and asked folks if they needed their clothes washed or ironed, or their houses cleaned, just so that we wouldn't starve. He would wake up early and drive down our main street all the way downtown and pick people up and drop them off, and he would make extra money that way. He would be back home by 10 to rest, and be back out by 4 and do it all over again for a few dollars.

On the weekends, he played in a band, and that was decent money, and we kept at it until things got better and had a few dollars saved up. We did what we needed to do to keep a roof over our heads and food on the table for our children.

We went through all of that, and this is what my husband was doing? We were finally in a place where our kids were grown, were almost finished with college. We should have been planning our children's weddings and getting ready for our grandchildren, and this is what he was doing to me, to us, to our children, family, and our church!

No! I couldn't believe it! It took me about five years to accept that his indiscretion wasn't a one-time thing. And even though it would have hurt if it was just one time, I was ready to forgive, talk to our bishop and move on.

My breaking point came when I came back early one day from seeing my baby girl in school. She was having some issues, and I had gone down to see her. I had a feeling that day that I needed to get home early. I got home and who was sitting in my living room? –Her! I was very gracious and pleasant, and I even offered her something to drink.

It was as if I was having an out-of-body experience. I couldn't believe that my husband would have the audacity to bring this woman into our home. And that was it! The next day while he was out doing whatever, I packed my important papers, some clothes, some pictures of the kids and other keepsakes, got in my car, and drove off!

I walked away from a 30-year marriage, and all the benefits that came with it. I left my husband! And then he married her! So, is there a secret? I don't know! I did everything right. I stuck by him, fed him, sexed him, clothed him, prayed for him, took care of him when he was sick, believed in him when no one else did, and my childhood sweetheart did that to me!

42 Years

*E*very time I tell the story about my husband and me, it brings a smile to my face. Well, we were in college, and that was my first time being away from home. I loved my new-found freedom.

I had a boyfriend that I didn't tell Daddy about, but somehow, he heard about it, and he came up to the school to meet my new boyfriend. We met at a restaurant, and my boyfriend was just trembling and sweating. An hour later, Daddy had to get back home to pick up momma on time from the train station. When he got up, he kissed, hugged me, and said my first and middle name. Now that meant — "Don't you dare!" That made my heart sink because I knew then that he didn't like him.

Later, I called Daddy and asked him how he liked my boyfriend and told him that he was studying to be a doctor. Daddy said, "Baby, why don't you wait on the Lord?" My Daddy didn't like him! But we kept courting, and so on.

There was this guy that was eyeing me and talking to me here and there, but I had no interest in him because I had my doctor-to-be boyfriend. Somehow, he found out that my Daddy was a Baptist preacher, so he came to Easter Service. And he was just a-grinning at me.

After church, I got home with my older brothers and who was sitting in my living room? The weird guy! I almost turned around and ran. My Dad jumped up, smiling from ear to ear, and called me into the living room and said, "This is Paul, a pastor's son from Mississippi. He said he goes to your school?"

I tried to be gracious and pleasant. Then here comes Momma with a cola for them and hot cup of cocoa for me. Now in those days, cocoa was only for special occasions, or you were going to die. So, I looked at Momma, and she was just grinning and smiling from ear to ear and staring at me weird.

Then Daddy said, "Brother Paul here has come to ask me if he could take you out for dinner one evening." In my mind, I was crying, because I knew that Daddy and Momma liked him, and then my brothers started to smile, and I was the only one without a smile. So, I agreed to go to dinner with him later when back at school.

The long and short of it is that my Daddy talked me into breaking up with my boyfriend, and on New Year's Eve, Mr. Weird Guy proposed at church. I have never seen my Daddy so happy! Paul had graduated the May before, and I would graduate the following May. Both Daddy and Momma were adamant about me finishing school, and so in July, I became Mrs. Paul. Looking back, I do not regret it. Yes, my former boyfriend went on to become a doctor.

(Read First Lady Counsel in back.)

50 Years

*I*n our 50 years of marriage, my husband and I have never argued. Never! I have never argued with my husband or disagreed with him, or questioned him. That was the secret to my parents staying married, and my mother taught me to never argue with my husband.

Not about the kids, money, nothing. Whatever he says goes; he says jump and I ask how high. Have sex whenever he wants; don't question his whereabouts, nothing. And, when he comes home, don't question him on where he was and why he didn't call. When money is missing from the account, let it be, don't ask about it.

When we were younger, he would disappear for days. I never asked him where he was. When he came home, I acted like a happy wife and took his coat and shoes, and made him something to eat.

When it comes to the church, I just sit there and be a lovely First Lady. When the women want to talk to my husband, I sit and wait for him to finish, and I don't ask any questions.

When it came to the kids, whatever he said went. When my daughters needed new clothes, bras, underwear, I would tell them to ask their daddy! The same thing goes for the boys.

Breakfast, lunch, and dinner — I made his plate and served him first. When he was late for dinner, I would make the kids wait until he got in before I let them eat. If it'd been about an hour, I would let them eat, but I would wait for him to come home before I ate.

And we have been going 50 years strong and still going. Wives these days need to learn to be quiet and just let their husbands be. Stop questioning him and wanting him to talk to them, and all that stuff. It worked for us!

Am I happy? Well, it's not about my happiness, it's about the happiness of my husband. And as long as he is happy, I'm good. God created me to please him and make him happy. It's not about me, and what I want, it's about my husband.

JANICE HYLTON-THOMPSON

20 Plus, Years of Marriage

34

20 Years

*W*hen we were getting the couple's massage, he said he needed to tell me something, but then we got on to something else. The next day while on the golf course, he said, "Look, we've been very unhappy in our marriage, and we've both done things. We haven't been happy in a long time. We haven't been happy since college."

I wasn't paying attention to what he was saying because it just sounded like the same old conversation and gibberish he's been saying for God knows how long. Then he said, "So I'm going to have a baby."

The golf club fell out of my hand, and I went numb for a second. Then I took up the club and went after him asking what did he say.

Have you ever been hurt so bad that it feels as if you can never recover? How can the man who got down on one knee, asked your father for your hand in marriage, watched you walk down the aisle, professed his love and commitment to you, and stood before God and man at the Lord's holy altar and took vows, then turn around and hurt you like that? And then to tell me that on our "20th anniversary?"

30 Years

*M*y son didn't come around for a day or two, and that was a bit suspicious because he always came by every day. As his mother, I felt that something was wrong, so I called around and no one had seen him. Called the police station to see if he got locked up, and he wasn't there. Finally, I called the morgue after another few days and described the tattoos on his body, and sadly he was there.

My son was murdered and his body mutilated! Words cannot express the pain and hurt that I felt. Only a mother that has lost a child the way I did can understand that pain.

That same evening, my husband of over 30 years told me that he was leaving me for his girlfriend whom he had fallen head over heels in love with and that he wanted to be with her.

Surprisingly, 'her' turned out to be a 'he.' So not only was my baby murdered, but my husband told me on that same day that he was leaving me for a man.

30 *Years*

*C*an you believe it? In a few years, I will be 100 years old. After 30 years of marriage, I realized that if I didn't leave my husband, I would end up in the poor house, and that was something I couldn't do. He was in the military. One day, he came home and asked my father for my hand in marriage. My dad asked me if I wanted to go and I said "yes." But honestly, I was hoping that he would say, "No! She cannot move up north with you."

We had a little church wedding and came up north. He was strange and secretive. One day I went to the bank to take some money out to get something for one of the kids. The teller told me that I couldn't take any money out because my name wasn't on the account. When I asked him, he said that he would put my name on it whenever I started to work. Later, I found out that my name wasn't on anything. Not the house, business or anything else.

For 30 years, I stayed and struggled with him and his irresponsible ways with money. We would go without food, lights, and a few times, heat in the winter. When he was sick, some bills came to our home, and I opened them. He had taken out second mortgages on the house and business without telling me. One Friday night, two men came to my home claiming that he owed them money. It came to light that he had been gambling at casinos and horse-betting and so on. Then the bank came for the house.

That was it! I realized that if I didn't divorce him, I would end up in the poor house. At 50, I divorced him. I walked away empty-handed because he had gambled everything we had. I went back to school and got a certificate and worked for years and retired at almost 80. I was able to purchase two properties, of which one I sold a few years ago. I had paid $30k for one, and in those days that was a lot of money. But I was able to sell that one for almost ten times what I paid for it and bought my retirement home.

JANICE HYLTON-THOMPSON

Today, at almost 100, I am still living a very comfortable life with my pension and investments, and my social security is a plus. Divorcing him was the best decision of my life. I encourage young women to look out for themselves if he is not doing the right thing. If I hadn't left my husband, I would have ended up in the poor house as he did. Sometimes, you try your best to hold on to your marriage, but it does take both of you working at it to make it work. My marriage is proof that it needed both of us.

35 Years

I must be the only woman in the whole wide world who isn't mad that her husband ran off with another woman. Excuse me, a *younger* woman. Thank you, Jesus! That is a burden taken off my shoulders. "It's his midlife crisis," his momma says! Honey, he can have his midlife crisis out of my life. I'm not going to divorce him because I have his pension, ROTH IRA, and social security coming, and when and if he dies before me, I have a fat insurance check coming! I have already split mine up so the kids can get most of it if I go before him.

The house is paid for; the children are out of college, and I am enjoying my grandchildren and my new freedom. I might even start to date, but I just don't want to be bothered with grumpy old men and saggy dingalings! He's been a fool since he turned fifty. After thirty-five years of marriage, he got up and ran off with some new young thang. Fine with me, enjoy her! She has taken him off my hands.

You know what the sad thing is? He couldn't even keep up with me in the bedroom even when he was twenty. In thirty-five years, he has never been able to keep up or outdo me. But I stayed and stuck it through for the sake of my children and him.

40 Years

*M*y parents just "celebrated" forty years of marriage. As much as I love them, I think they are so fake. My father has cheated on my mother for years. There are even outside children, and I can't understand for the life of me what they are "celebrating." They live in separate parts of the house, they can't stand each other, they don't even talk to each other half the time, but my sister throws them a forty-year celebration party?

I didn't attend the party! Later that week, Mom asked why I didn't participate, and I just told her how I felt. And I asked her why she stayed with Daddy all those years being miserable and unhappy. You know what she said to me? She said, "Baby, couples our age don't get divorced. Your Daddy has always been a good provider. He pays all the bills, we have food and clothing, and if I left, I wouldn't have had anything. He has always taken care of me, so I stayed."

She went on to say, "That's why I have pushed you and your sister so hard to go to school and to get a good job so that you don't have to depend on any man to take care of you or do anything for you. Plus, at my age, where am I going?"

42 Years

*M*arried forty-two years, and for the last six years, my husband has been shacking up with some floozy across town. I don't know what that heifer is doing sweety, because when he was over here "it" didn't work. I know he has been unfaithful our entire marriage. But you know, in those days, women didn't leave. He was in the military, and when he got out, he got a good government job. Plus, I didn't want to interrupt my children's life. I cried myself to sleep many nights because I stayed in the marriage for my kids.

Then he got sick and wanted to move back home so that I could take care of him. I laughed at him and asked why the woman he has been shacking up with couldn't take care of him? My son called begging me to take him back, and I said no!

I had been thinking of selling the house and moving to the city to help my daughter with the grandkids. That was my cue! I put up the house for sale and did estate sales on the weekends, and in six months the house was sold to a lovely young couple and their three children.

I split the profits up four ways, and I took fifty percent. The rest I gave to my daughter, son, and his portion I gave to our son for him. My daughter was so happy for the money because she had just gone through a divorce and had to sell their house and didn't get much out of it.

She was going through the same thing I had did as a young wife, and I told her, "Don't you waste your life waiting for that fool to get his stuff together. Once a cheater, always a cheater, and he will never change. Leave that fool and move on with your life. You are too young to give up on love and wait for him to do right."

She got her a beautiful condo in the city, and I got a lovely three-bedroom across town. This way, when my grandbabies come to visit for the summer, they have their space.

My daughter's ex-helps with the children, but when he can't drop them off to school, I drop them off and pick them up for her. I am enjoying my new life.

My husband, the fool, asked me if he could come and stay with me. I hung up the phone on him. Next time he asked what about my vows? I asked him what about his vows? For forty-two years, and especially the last six years, he was shacking up across town, so what about his vows? He couldn't answer.

How is it that our vows only seem to benefit the husbands? Now he is sick and needs a caretaker, and he wants to ask about vows? Then he wants to bring up God since I started going back to church with my daughter and grandbabies? I asked him where God was for forty-two years?

Anyway, my son got him into an excellent senior citizen's home with 24-hour care near him and his wife.

I was foolish for staying with him all these years, wasting my life, waiting for him to get it together. Life has passed me by! Who wants a 66-year-old woman in this day and time?

That's why I told my daughter to not stay with her cheating husband. Let that fool go so she can find someone else to share the rest of her life with.

55 Years

*J*ust celebrated my 74th birthday and had been married fifty-five years. My husband was in the military right out of high school. Back in those days, that is what you did. We had three beautiful children, and he spent a lot of time overseas. Once, he came home to visit and in about a week or so I was itching and burning. I just didn't know what was going on with me.

At that time, I was a nanny for a nurse. I asked her about it, and she told me to go to the doctor. I don't even remember what they said it was, but it was some sexually transmitted disease.

I was so distraught! I confronted my husband, and he denied it and blamed it on me, saying that I had been cheating while he was in the military. I packed my stuff, took my kids, and went to my parents. They sent me back home and told me to go work it out with my husband.

Went back home and didn't talk to him, and only called him after six months when he didn't send any money for me and kids. I had decided that I would stay with him until my baby turned 18 and went to college.

But, over the years, we both came to know Jesus, and he said he was trying to do better, and so I stayed. But honestly, that is still in the back of my mind. I know wives say they forgive and forget, but I don't understand how you forget something like that.

62 Years

*M*y parents have been married 62 years and separated for 38 years. Neither of them ever told us what happened, but to my knowledge, Mom always wanted to go to school and Daddy didn't want her to go.

Finally, when I went off to college, she signed up for classes at the local community college and Daddy moved out. I came home for Thanksgiving and Daddy, and his things were gone, and Mommy was staying up late studying. She became a kindergarten teacher and a librarian. She always loved teaching children, and books.

Daddy never came back home, and 38 years later, they are still separated. Mom lives with my husband and me. She is older now and I don't trust her to be alone. Dad lives not too far from here, comes by a few times per week and I check on him often. I have tried to get him to come here and live with us, but he refuses.

Couples back in those days didn't get a divorce. They just lived separated for years if the marriage wasn't reconciled. And usually, if it was reconciled, it was because one of them was sick and needed the other to help out.

So yes, my parents have been separated for almost 40 years.

Abuse

Daughter to the Slaughter

I was 16 years old, and he was 24 when my mother forced me to marry him because he was well off and had his own house and business. My father didn't want me to get married, but my mom insisted. On the day I was to get married, I ran away, and they found me, dressed me, and brought me to the church. I remember my father crying and saying, "They are carrying my daughter to the slaughter." I sincerely wish he was a stronger man who would have stood up to my mother. I cried all the way through the wedding. I was just a kid; I wasn't ready to be married.

The abuse physically, verbally, and sexually started right away. I was a virgin, and he was an experienced 24-year-old man who didn't care whether I was a virgin or not. I got pregnant and eventually had two boys. Throughout this time, I faced abuse in every way—even starvation.

When I was pregnant with my third child, it got worse. It was so bad that he tried to throw me down the hole of the outhouse. In those days, we didn't have indoor toilets. Thank God, my belly was so big that he couldn't get me down the hole. He abused me more and more, and I lost that child who is buried on the land he still owns today. He will not sell it since our son is buried there.

During this time, I would run away and go home, and my mother would always send me back. The last time was when my oldest son was about three years old. While he was beating me, our son was hitting him, and he kicked my baby across the room. As his little lifeless body laid in a corner, I started fighting him with everything I had.

He threw me out, burned my clothes, boarded up the house, and took our sons to his grandmother's house. I had no choice but to go home, and I guess God touched my mother's heart and she allowed me to stay. A week later, my sister and I went to his grandmother's house and stole my boys. She ran after us while we ran into the bushes with them.

THE NAKED WIFE

Twenty years later, at my youngest son's wedding, I was nervous and trembling that I had to be in the same room with him. I was terrified. Thirty-five years later, he asked me to marry him again. Would you believe that?

JANICE HYLTON-THOMPSON

Coming to America

I was only 15 years old when he set his eyes on me, but the legal age in the Islands for a man to marry a young girl is 16. As soon as I turned 16, he came home from America, and my mother was so stupid that she gave me to him just because he promised to bring me to America and take her up there. I was disgusted! Can you imagine being 16 and a 37-year-old man being on top of you? I am grossed out even now, and my skin is crawling all over again.

At 17, he finally brought me to the United States, and that's where the abuse started. I had long dreads hanging all the way down my back right up to my bottom. But he cut my hair, saying that people would compliment me on how pretty I was and how beautiful my hair was. He signed me up for college, and he attended too to keep his eyes on me. He had his mother living downstairs from us to keep an eye on me while he worked at night.

During this time, I endured rape and abused — physically, sexually, emotionally, verbally, and psychologically. I couldn't have any friends because he claimed they were trying to poison my mind against him. People would be shocked when he introduced me as his wife and weirdly looked at us. That's where I learned the word "pedophile." I wasn't sure what it meant because I had never heard that word in the Islands. When I looked it up, it made sense to me, and that was where I started planning and gained my strength.

I was always book-smart, so I put all my strength and energy in my books. After he would rape me at nights, I would get up, take a shower, and study for hours. I gave birth to two children, but I couldn't connect with them because to me, they were a result of me being raped. His mother took care of them most of the time, and I always made an excuse that I needed to study to get into the nurses' program.

Finally, I was accepted into the nursing program which is very challenging and competitive to get into. Two years went by, and I graduated at the top of my class. The day I graduated was the day I left my pedophile rapist husband and the children that resulted, and I haven't looked back. Almost 20 years later and countless hours of counseling, I reached out to the children who have refused to see or talk to me because their father told them that I ran away with a man and left them. Not true, but I understand and pray that in time we can break bread together.

Dirty Socks and Cold Soup

*O*ur marriage became violent in the last two years. My husband started throwing things, punching the TV, the wall, and so on. One night he came after me with a bread knife, after he threw a water bottle at me while I ran up the stairs to lock myself and our children in the bedroom. I called the marriage counselor, and she told me to get the kids and go to a hotel. That was a scary situation!

A week later, we had to go back home because he had taken all the money out of the joint account and the credit cards were all maxed out. We didn't speak to each other for two weeks. Things went back to normal, but it would only be until the next fight or argument. Well, it wasn't too long after that before the next fight. He had some dirty socks in his hands that he threw in my face. I had a cup of cold soup in my hand, and I threw it in his face. Then I ran and locked the door.

Once again, I got on the phone with the marriage counselor and she suggested I call the police since he was banging on the door and threatening to kill me. I hung up with her to call the cops and told him that I was calling the police. He went on to curse me out, but I didn't call the police because if he got arrested his mother would have suffered because he paid all her bills.

The marriage counselor called me back, and I explained to her why I hadn't called. She encouraged me to leave. I explained that I couldn't afford to move and that I didn't make that much. She suggested I call my dad.

It bothered me to call my father because he had told me not to marry him. I called daddy, and in less than an hour, he was at my house with a few of his friends and their cars and trucks. He told me to grab what I could and leave. He paid for the kids and me to stay in a hotel for a month until we found an apartment, which he paid six months upfront for us. He figured that by then, child support should kick in and with my income, we could afford to live. Thank God for my daddy!

One Tear

I had just had our daughter and this time I think I had postpartum depression. I started going to counseling, but the counselor said she didn't think I had PPD. It sounded as if I was stressed out and that I needed to rest and get someone to help with the kids.

I took her advice. But, while I was home on maternity leave, I didn't get as much done as I wanted around the house. I was reading a lot, watching a lot of Bible teaching series to build myself up in the Lord and enjoying my baby.

The downstairs was a mess and had been a mess all week. My mom came over to drop our son off at daycare, and take Abigail for the day. Once she left, I got a burst of energy and cleaned the entire second floor.

I changed the sheets, did the floor, cleaned the bathrooms, even changed the curtains and changed our room around. Next thing I knew, I heard the doorbell, and it was mom with the kids. I couldn't believe the whole day was gone, but I felt good because I got a lot done and even Mom, was surprised.

An hour later mom left, and my husband came home. I was downstairs playing with the kids on the floor, and I had some dinner in the oven. He came in and went off! He cursed me out so bad; I couldn't believe it. It was so bad our son, who was five years old, came over and hugged me after he peed on himself. As one tear rolled down my cheek, he went upstairs and slammed the door.

I waited to see if he would come back down, seeing that the upstairs was beautiful. An hour later — nothing. I had put some laundry in earlier, I took the things out of the drier, got the kids, my purse, and I left. Seeing my little boy crying, peeing on himself and hugging me made me realize that, that was not the way to live. It wasn't the first time my husband had cursed me out like that in front of our son. That day I decided that that would be the last time!

JANICE HYLTON-THOMPSON

The Grip of Fear

*M*y four-year-old daughter was playing house, and she was acting like the husband. She slapped the doll and told it to shut up. Fear gripped my heart, and I knew I had to get my children and run for our lives. I had sat there for years and allowed my husband to abuse me. My children were seeing him beating and abusing me physically, verbally, and psychologically. I didn't realize that my kids were learning how to be an abusive mate.

I knew that he wouldn't let us go, as he often said if I left he would kill us. I had a friend at work who once caught me covering up my black eye with makeup, and she told me that I deserved better. I told her that I depended on him for our every need, and that I was lucky he was allowing me to work that little part-time job while the kids were in school. And even those few little dollars, he controlled.

She offered to help because she too had been in that situation at one time and she still has a limp today from how much he beat her. By God's grace and mercy, one morning while walking the kids to school, I made a dash for it. I just had to get out. I wrote a letter to my Mom, and to the police to let them know that we were not missing, but I had to get out of an abusive marriage and that I would confirm our safety every three months.

That woman saved my life and the lives of my children. I would encourage every woman who is in an abusive relationship to get out! The next time he hits you; he might kill or paralyze you. And think about your children. Is it worth it to save face for the world while your children suffer?

I won't give too much information, but there are organizations out there that will help women to get out of abusive relationships. And help with housing, and lawyers to help you file for divorce and get custody of your children.

A Gun

*M*y husband had wanted a gun since forever. But I had always refused because he has a bad temper and can become violent at times. So, when he said he wanted a gun, I sat down and talked to him about how I didn't think it was in the best interest of the family for him to get a gun because of his temper.

I thought we understood each other and that he had changed his mind. But, a few months later, he said he was going to get one and went with his friend to a gun range.

I knew that was my cue to go because I knew he would kill me and probably the kids because of his temper. I have been dealing with him and his bad temper and have begged him to go for counseling. He has always refused, saying that nothing was wrong with him and that counseling was for crazy people.

Burn Baby Burn

*F*ighting and arguing was our norm, and we did it all the time. He would say he was going to kill me and I would say not if I killed him first.

This one Friday night, we had a big fight, and it got physical. I kicked him out of the house, and he threatened to burn the house down. The next day, my neighbor came knocking at my door because there was fire coming up from the basement.

Yes, my husband had tried to burn the house down with his children in it and me. If it weren't for God's grace and mercy, we would be dead!

JANICE HYLTON-THOMPSON

For the Sake of the Kids?

*M*y marriage is over! But, I have decided to sacrifice my life and stay with my husband for my kids' sake. Well, at least that's what the counselor, pastor, and my Momma said. But is it really for the good of the kids?

When Daddy comes home drunk and is cussing me out, why would I want to have my children around that? When we fight and call each other names, is that safe for our children? When he grabs me by my throat, and our children see that, what is that telling them? When he picks up other women with the kids in the car and he tells them not to tell Mom, is that what I want my children to see?

"You both need to learn to live with each other for the sake of the kids," the older folks say.

"Keyword — both," I tell them. It will take two of us working together to make this work for the kids. But, is this the environment I want my children to grow up in? Is this how I want my son to learn to treat his wife? Do I want my girls to see me staying in an abusive marriage and, in turn, think it is okay to be treated like this?

I will admit that staying is not all bad. My boss stayed until her kids turned eighteen and went off to college, and then she left. But they both agreed that they would work together for the sake of the kids. He watched the kids when she went out, and she watched them when he went out. They were living together but separate. They divorced peacefully, and they walked away knowing that they both tried to provide a stable home for their children.

Unfortunately, that is not possible here. This house is like World War III. For the sake of my children, I cannot and will not stay.

Merry Christmas

*W*hen most wives wake up to gifts under the tree on Christmas morning, I woke up to my husband dragging me out of the bed because he said he saw me looking at our neighbor when I got out of the car the previous day. Most wives probably got pearls, fake or real, but I got the scar where he tried to cut my neck. Some wives probably got diamond earrings that match their eyes, but I have two black eyes.

What have I ever done to deserve being treated like this? He said I was worthless and that no one would want me! He said he would kill me if I ever left him. He said he would take my babies away from me if I ever tried to leave, and that was why he kept my little one with him most of the time. Plus, he is a man of influence, and he said he would have "his friends of influence" watching me and the house at all times, and that he had them all over the place.

But where there is a God, there is a way. One night he went out and got drunk for his birthday and came home late. I was wondering if that was the night I could run with the kids. He came back around 3 a.m., and around 5, he woke up screaming, throwing up, and pooping. I ran downstairs to see and help him, but a voice spoke to me and said — RUN!

I ran back upstairs, woke the kids, grabbed backpacks that I had already packed and hid, and about $3000 I had saved up, a $1 here, $10 there. We ran down the back stairs, and I told the kids to run until they got to the train. My babies ran so fast; it was as if they had skates on. When we got to the train, it was already there, and the conductor looked as if he was waiting for us. He was looking our direction, and he said, "Get on."

All the way to the end of Penn Station, the conductor stared and stared at us. I was nervous, thinking he might know my husband, but then he nodded his head, smiled, came over and handed me a bag and said, "God bless you and your children!" In the bag were train tickets, a disposable phone, addresses to women's shelters, water, bread, and a Bible.

I was so nervous that someone might be following us that for the whole day we jumped on different trains to lose anyone, or my husband if he was following us. I was so afraid! The kids began to get weary, so I checked us into a hotel two states away, fed them, and put them to bed after we knelt and prayed and thanked the Lord for His goodness. I grabbed the Bible the conductor gave me and opened it. It opened to $1000 and that was when I broke down.

Can I tell you that every step of the way God kept and provided for us? It was as if He was waiting for me to take the first step! Finally, I came back to our state and checked into one of the women's shelters, and they helped me to get an attorney, got my divorce and full custody of the kids. He can get visitation after he completes domestic violence counseling. I did not know that there is a new law now that states if there is domestic violence in the home, children's services can take the children.

I am so grateful to God who ordered our steps!

12 Kids, a 38 Shot Gun & a 9 MM

I met this awesome guy who was great with my kids. I was impressed because I always wanted to get married. But in my mind, was a lingering question: who would marry me with six children? This man was simply remarkable and accepted me and all of my children?

Everything was great until one day I was pinned against the wall, with a blow to my stomach and our first baby was gone. Feeling trapped, I didn't know how to tell my mom. So, I disappeared for twelve hours while the cops searched for me. I had been in an abusive relationship before, and I knew that this was not going to get any better. Even though, I hoped it would. So I attempted to leave Mr. Awesome, and that was unsuccessful.

The second attempt of leaving, he stole my keys, threatened to kill himself, and then threw a pot of hot oil and frying pork chops at me that burned my arm, hands, and face. My family's version of trying to help me was to call Child Protective Services. But I hid because I was not going to allow anyone to split my kids and me up.

I struggled to find a place for us, and thankfully the Lord made a way. But then he found us! He beat me, tore off my clothes and he raped me. Then someone broke into my house, stole my rent money and the kids Wii. So, what did I do? I went back to him. But then, he cheated and brought a girl in our bed, and this time I decided that I wouldn't take him back.

That upset him, so he elbowed me in my face, gave me two black eyes and thank God for his cousin who saved me! But he threatened that he would kill his cousin if I didn't come back to him.

So, I went back, and three months later, I was pregnant with my third pregnancy for him. This time, however, I decided that I wouldn't miscarry, and I took off to stay with my aunt but came back in time to deliver the baby.

But guess what I did ladies, after all the abuse and abandonment, I still went ahead and married him because of the baby!!? He continued to abuse my children and me. I despised him, the thought and looks of him. I tried to leave again, but he had my son in the air by his throat, with a 38 in his hand. He said I wasn't leaving with his baby.

After that, he had me isolated. I had contact with no one, not even my mom who I used to talk to daily. So, my family faked being the state police doing a welfare check. And that day, I grabbed my babies, and I ran. But, I was also pregnant and that time I reported the abuse and rape to the police and I got a restraining order. If he saw us, it was supervised by one of my family members.

Eight months pregnant, my sister had to go to work, and he had me up on the wall again, by my throat. I felt helpless, but then I felt sorry for him and made excuses for him. Should I leave or stay? Maybe in time, he will go? I want to leave, but I remain.

Perhaps, in time he will grow, stop, maybe I can teach him? He loves me, I know he does, he's just had a rough life, I forgive him. Then I was double minded! Don't trust him, don't leave him around the kids, don't be with him alone!

And then one day, a light came on for me, and I noticed something! If someone was around, he could control himself and then I realized that him abusing me was a choice. A lifestyle he grew up in, he sees nothing wrong with it.

I stayed because I had already had six kids with no daddy; I didn't want that for these too. So, I stayed three more years! Three more years of chances, abuse both physically and emotionally. Financial burdens, stress, worries, other woman and other children and him not working.

Unfortunately, now my beautiful 12 children and I are living in a bubble because of Child Protective Services. The last straw was when he came after me with a 9mm gun. A few months ago, he grabbed me by my neck and tried to strangle me. Three months later, I still have those marks on my neck, and every time I look in the mirror, I see them.

I would encourage every young woman who is dating to pay attention to everything. If you get in a marriage and the abuse begins, leave. Don't waste your life and time, because you are worthy. So don't allow anyone to take your worth away.

THE NAKED WIFE

For a long time, I struggled with staying in the marriage because many churches don't believe in divorce. But, I'm getting a divorce, even God understands!

Fatty

fter three babies, two of which were C-section, my husband had
the nerve to call me Fatty! My issue with him calling me Fatty is
that he is no "Rock." He has a huge gut, and when I was pregnant, his belly
was bigger than mine. The man can't even see his little 'thing,' but he calls
me Fatty? When I was pregnant, I asked him repeatedly to come and walk
with me to encourage me. It could have been a way to spend time together
and worked out, but he said no, he was too tired. But he wants to call me
Fatty?

With my first baby, I only gained 20 pounds, plus I was younger then.
With my second baby, I gained 41 lbs, and with my last pregnancy, I gained
about 75 lbs. It was a bit high-risk, so I couldn't work out or walk as much
as I wanted to. With both first and second, I lose the weight in less than a
year, but with this last one, it's a bit harder.

We have a neighborhood walking group. A few of us walk together in
the morning on our main road. Usually, I would leave the kids while he was
still there and go walking, but then he started leaving for work at 6 a.m. just
so that he wouldn't have to watch the kids. Did I mention that he didn't
need to be at work at 9 a.m.?

I was determined, so I pushed the older kids in the stroller while my
neighbor pushed the baby. My father was visiting one day, and he heard
him call me Fatty. Later, Daddy called me and asked if he had heard my
husband call me Fatty. After an hour on the phone, Daddy said he would
pay for me to have a personal trainer until I lose the weight I wanted to.

One day while I was working out with my trainer, he came home and
cursed my trainer and me out, and told her never to set foot in his house
again. So, we worked out at my neighbor's house, and she got some lessons,
too. While I was getting smaller, he was getting bigger, because he refused
to eat the healthy meals I was making.

Six months later, I was almost back to the weight I was when I got
married. I dressed up in the dress I wore on our first date, put my hair up

THE NAKED WIFE

in a bun, and came down the stairs. My husband was standing at the foot of the stairs and looked as if he had seen a ghost. He asked "where are you going? "Leaving you!" I said.

JANICE HYLTON-THOMPSON

DOMESTIC VIOLENCE

National Domestic Violence Number
1 800-799-7223
1-800 787 3224 TTY

If you are a woman reading this and are in a domestic violence situation, I want to tell you that you are worth so much more. God did not create you to be beaten by your husband.

God created you to be loved and cherished, protected and provided for by him.

Your husband should never raise his hands to hit you, but he is to bless you with them.

Your husband must never kick you, but he should walk the Word of God before you.

Your husband should never use his tongue to curse and belittle you, but he should speak of greatness to you and your children.

Your husband should not use his influence to hold you in bondage, but he should show you off.

Please, seek help if you or your children are being abused!

Adultery/Infidelity

Champagne Glasses, Lip Gloss & Thongs

T he first time we met, there was something special about my husband. He had charisma, and his presence commanded attention. It was at a realtor's conference that I attended with my friend, who had insisted that I get out of the house, so I could make myself available to be found.

I walked in the room, and our eyes met. I pretended as if I didn't even see him and avoided him all evening, but sneaked a peek here and there. When we were leaving, he spoke, and we exchanged business cards. We were inseparable the entire weekend.

Surprisingly, we didn't live far from each other, and over the next year, we got to know each other along with our families. Daddy, along with my family and friends, liked him and insisted that he was the one. He was a man of God, a tither, and he was perfect for me.

We completed pre-marital counseling, and almost two years later, we were married. It was a beautiful church wedding, all paid for by my Daddy! We didn't get to have a honeymoon because he had another realtor's conference coming up. But we did spend the weekend together, and then he was off to work.

Two months after our wedding, he was away, and I surprised him. The management lets me in his room; I was shocked. On the table were two wine glasses, one of which had shimmering lip gloss, and two different bottles of wine. I couldn't believe it, so I went and sat on the couch. His luggage was lying next to it and sticking out were a pair of thongs! My heart sank, and tears ran down my face.

I sat there in the dark until he came in, and the look on my face said it all. I confronted him, and he denied it and said the lip-gloss was his chapstick. The ironic thing about that was that I had to stay on him all winter about wearing ChapStick, but in the heat of August, he was wearing some?

And the thongs, I asked? He said someone was trying to frame him - that he didn't cheat and had been faithful. Every fiber of my being told me he was lying while he went down on his knees and begged me to believe him. I slept on the couch, got up the next morning, and left.

I couldn't stand to lose him though, so I forgave him and decided to give him another chance. Five years and two babies later, there have been several instances and proofs of his infidelities, but I am so ashamed that I cannot bring myself to tell my Daddy or to leave him.

He does provide a decent life for the kids and me, and even though I have threatened to leave a thousand times, I just can't bring myself to leave him. I think I care too much about what the church and people would think. And what would my Daddy say?

JANICE HYLTON-THOMPSON

The Elder's Mistress

*M*arried 15 years, and my husband has been cheating on me the whole time with his mistress. Her name is the Church. Yes, the Church is my husband's mistress. I love his love, zeal, and compassion for the Church and the members. But my husband puts the Church before our children and me. It got so bad that he threatened to put me out if I didn't get with the program.

Every time someone called, no matter what time of the night it was, he would go. Whenever someone had a need, he used our money with no discussion with me to pay their rent, car note, groceries, and so on. I believe in giving, but there must be a limit. When the children and I had to go without so that others could have, I could not believe that was God. Especially when I was the one who went to a physical job every day to work.

He worked here and there in construction and had money when the Church gave an offering, but the consistent income was mine. So, when my children couldn't get what they wanted because daddy used our money for the Church folks, I had a huge issue with that. And I do not believe it is the Will of God for anyone to put the Church in front of his wife and children.

A week later after Church, it was raining, and the kids and I were sitting in the car. He told us to get out and wait until he dropped the church-people home and then he would come back for us. Someone else dropped us home, and I confronted him about the way he treated us. Our neighbors called the police because we were arguing and fighting. The police came and told him to leave, or else they would arrest us both. He left and came back later.

The straw that broke the camel's back was when he wanted me to give him $500 out of my pay to pay a Sister's rent in the Church. I told him "No" because I needed the money to buy back-to-school clothes for the children. He grabbed me and slapped me! I don't know where the strength came from, but I fought him back as if he had stolen something!!

THE NAKED WIFE

And then I called the police, and they locked him up. He called me and asked me to bail him out. I told him to call all of the church-people he had been spending our money on. That was my chance to pack up our things, and we moved. I didn't have the money to get an apartment, so I moved in with my sister for about a year until I could afford an apartment.

Self-Esteem

*O*nly a wife whose husband has been unfaithful understands the pain and hurt of deception, rejection, and betrayal. A husband's adulterous ways affect you as a wife and as a woman. It causes you to question your self-worth. You begin to ask yourself, "What's wrong with me? Am I not enough? Doesn't he like me as a woman, a wife? Does he not like my body?"

"Does he not like to have sex with me? Maybe instead of staying celibate for years, perhaps I should have been getting more experience. At least, I could have been more experienced in our marriage bed."

You look in the mirror, and instead of seeing the confident woman you once were, you look into the eyes of a woman who is unsure of herself. You begin to think of all of the sacrifices you made to choose him, all of the guys you passed up for him, only for him to turn around and treat you like trash.

Then, you begin to think of all the types of women who have been cheated on. Some of the most beautiful and attentive women have been cheated on by their husbands. Women who have had ten children for their husbands have also been cheated on and left high and dry by their husbands.

Rich, poor, fat, skinny, black, white, stay-at-home moms, and working women, all have been cheated on by their husbands. It causes depression along with self-esteem and identity issues. But then, you look deep into your eyes and remember that you are not the one that broke your vows, but he did, and you have nothing to be ashamed of.

After the pain, hurt and tears, you begin to realize that you need to take time for yourself and get to know you again. How beautiful you are. How sweet, kind, tender, and sensitive you are. And that you are not in control of what another adult does.

It will take time, but with your feminine grace, remembering who you are in Christ, you will realize that you are a gift. Your husband didn't treat you as such, but that doesn't mean your value changed. You are now worth more, and maybe just a step of faith will help you to get back out there again.

What?

*W*here did the idea come from that wives should suck it up and stay with a cheating husband? He goes out and commits adultery, but I decided to leave, and I'm being blamed for breaking up the family? I'm the one destroying the family because I know that I'm worth more than a man that can't keep his ding-a-ling in his pants? I know I don't deserve to be treated like this. Why should I sit and take it?

Then people tell you to stay so you can keep your family together. Family? Why is the burden on me to keep my family together when he is the one that didn't care about the family and cheated?

Oh, give him time to get it right, some have said! More time? You mean my time? I need to sit for God knows how long and wait for him to decide to be faithful to his wife and family? And what do I do when it has been 20 years, and he still needs more time to get his stuff right? I think 20 years is more than enough time, don't you? I have already wasted 20 years; he will not get another second. Enough is enough!

And do you know what the messed-up thing is? If a wife cheats on her husband, he can't take it. He will pack up and leave her in a second without trying to save the marriage. She is looked down on, called all kind of names and shunned for cheating on her husband. But when it's the husband the wife is often told: "oh work it out, men will be men."

Just Following My Head

$\mathcal{M}$y husband and I went to our Pastor and First Lady for counseling because I caught him cheating. Our meeting went a little like this:

Pastor: Why are you guys here?

Husband: Well, Pastor, I messed up, and she went to file for divorce.

Pastor: Wait, wait one second! Did you file for divorce?

First Lady: What do you mean, you messed up?

Husband: Well, I kind of cheated!

Wife: He cheated!

Pastor: He cheated, and you filed for divorce?

Wife: Yes, sir!

Pastor: Well, why is it that your first action was to file for divorce? Why didn't you come and see us first?

Wife: Excuse me? Yes, I went to file for divorce!

Pastor: Sister Sophia, the first action after your husband messes up is not to see your lawyer. The first step should be prayer, grace, and counseling. You going to file for divorce says you were not committed to the marriage and you never loved your husband! You've been married for two years, and you are ready to throw in the towel?

First Lady: Amen! That was very selfish of you!

Wife: Excuse me? Let me see if I heard you both correctly. My husband cheated, broke our wedding vows, but I'm the one that's selfish, not committed, and I'm being chastised? Are ya'll serious? I didn't cheat! I was faithful this whole time!

Why didn't he come and see you before he got involved with this woman? Why didn't my husband pray and have grace? Why didn't he tell that woman that he was committed to his marriage and he loves his wife and family?

Pastor: Now, now, wait a minute. We are not chastising you; all we are saying is that you have to fight for your marriage!

First Lady: Right.

Wife: Why didn't he fight for his marriage? Everything you are telling me, you need to look at him and tell him! I am not at fault here! I was faithful this whole time. When he laid down with her, it tells me that he doesn't love me, doesn't care, doesn't want the marriage, he wasn't committed, and the marriage was over!

First Lady: Baby, men cheat for different reasons!

Pastor: Exactly! And, because he cheated, doesn't mean he doesn't love you, isn't committed, and doesn't want the marriage!

Husband: Right, sir, I love my wife!

Wife: So, because men cheat for different reasons, what does that mean? Does that mean I need to stay with him and accept his behavior because men cheat for various reasons? I don't care why men cheat. When we stood at that altar, that was a sign of commitment to me and me alone. If he wasn't able to keep that commitment, he should not have asked me to marry him!

Pastor: Sister, yes, but people make mistakes, and just like God gave you another chance, you need to give this brother another chance!

Wife: Another chance?

Husband: Yes baby, I didn't mean to cheat. You know I love you, and I don't want you to leave me!

Wife: Sorry, you won't get another chance to cheat on me! No, you don't love me, and you should have thought about the consequences before you cheated! You were texting, talking on the phone, going out for dinner, etc., and you didn't think about me then? You didn't think, 'I love my wife, and I shouldn't be doing this?'

Husband: Baby, I love you.

Pastor: Sister, your husband loves you.

First Lady: Yes, he does!

Wife: Really?

Husband: Yes, baby!

Wife: That's funny because love should have made you not cheat! Love should have made you keep your ding-a-ling in your pants! I deserve better! You don't deserve me! Love is what love does!

THE NAKED WIFE

I'm the victim here, but I'm being chastised? Are ya'll serious? And he didn't confess to me; he didn't come to me and say, baby, I messed up! I found used condoms in his truck, and when I confronted him, he denied it and blamed it on one of his boys!

When he felt like cheating, why didn't he come to you guys and say Pastor help me! Am I being tempted to cheat? Why didn't he come to me and tell me? Why didn't he beg me to help him then? And now that he got caught, he wants to run to you and beg me to stay? Oh, no! Once a cheater he will always be a cheater. And since you like to cheat for different reasons, you should be glad that I'm giving you your walking papers, so you can be free to have as many women as you like!

First Lady: (clutches her pearls with eyes wide open.)

Pastor: Sister Sophia, now wait one minute, let's put things into perspective.

Wife: (gets up and walks out, then turns around) Pay me my child support and sign the papers when you get them!

(Husband hangs head and begins to tear up.)

(Wife walks out and slams the door!)

Can you believe that they blamed me for the breakup of the family? Something is seriously wrong with that guilt trip. He goes out and cheats several times, but I am being blamed? That is not right at all!!

Leaving him was the best thing I have done. About two years later, God blessed me with a wonderful husband, we are very open and honest with each other, and ten years later, I am the happiest woman on earth.

Competition

*M*y husband asked me to marry him, but now I need to compete with other women for him? That doesn't make sense to me. He can go ahead and do what he wants to do, and I will do what I need to do for our children and me.

He told me one day, maybe if I did what all those other women did, then he wouldn't have to go out there and do what he does. Excuse me? Ladies, when I got married, I was a fool in love. I did everything to keep my husband happy. I remember one year for our anniversary; I spread red roses from the door to the couch and all the way up to our bedroom.

In the living room, I had a glass of red wine, his favorite meal, and I was on bended knee, taking care of him. I would swing on the chandeliers just to make him happy and satisfied, but the more I did, the more he did his dirt outside.

When I met him, he had nothing; he was working for another mechanic, fixing cars. He was living in his aunt's basement where he didn't even have heat. He asked me out, and we started talking. Two years later, we were married because I thought this man was hard-working and had some potential. I helped him to work on his credit, and even then, he couldn't get a business loan. So, I took one out on my credit and helped him start his own mechanic's shop.

When he didn't have any money coming in, and business was slow when he started, I paid all the bills and held us down. Now he wants to cheat and act like I don't exist? No money is coming in, because when the women come over to get their cars fixed, instead of him letting them pay, he has them doing him sexual favors. He ain't crap!

Double Standards

*A*fter ten years of marriage, my husband got some chick pregnant. He begged and pleaded for me to stay! After many sessions of counseling, I said if he wanted to try again then I was willing to try, too. I helped with his son and acted like that was my baby. I took care of the baby whenever he had him, with doctor's appointments and daycare. I had forgiven him and was willing to do anything to save my marriage.

Three years later, he started his crap again. This time, I said I wasn't going to sit and take it. So, I messed around with my coworker that I was so incredibly attracted to that I could taste it. Let's be clear, I'm not saying this was the right thing to do, but this is my story.

I got pregnant, but it was not intentional or planned, but I was pregnant. When I told my wonderful husband, whom I had stood by and his baby, he insisted that I abort the child. We both knew it wasn't his because we were not having sex. My response was no!

Then he said if I kept the baby, he would leave me. So I helped him pack his stuff, and he moved in with his baby's momma! My beautiful son, Isaac Jr., is now seven years old. His father and I are great friends, and we parent him together. My ex is still pissed!

JANICE HYLTON-THOMPSON

What's Wrong with Me?

We were newlyweds, but my husband just didn't seem interested in me anymore. I wasn't sure what it was. I always kept myself clean, smelling good, hair, and nails done. I'm not a nagger or anything like that. I washed, cooked, and cleaned. Kept the house clean, always had his dinner ready when he came home, just like my Momma used to do for my Daddy.

But he just didn't seem interested in being with me. I noticed that he didn't even look at me the way he used to. It was as if he didn't even see me. So, I started going to the gym more. I took good care of myself; I wore sexy lingerie around the house and to bed. But, half the time he didn't come to bed till late. I didn't think he was cheating because he was a homebody, always there in his man cave.

One day, while he ran out to get some wine, I went into his man cave and there it was. Porn on his computer, all these young, almost teenage girls. There were so many of them! I called him, yelling and screaming, and he rushed home. I threw his computer at him, and he shoved me into the wall. So, I called the cops, and he was arrested because I had scratches and bruises on me.

I didn't press charges because I don't think he meant to hurt me. It was an accident. After a year of counseling, I decided that the marriage wouldn't work because he didn't change his way and many times, I was in the counseling sessions by myself. I do believe that porn is a trick of the devil and another enemy of marriages.

I Know

"*I* know that my wife loves me!" That's what he told the marriage counselor after I found text messages from an ex-girlfriend on his phone about their time together recently. That hurt, because some of the things he was texting her were things I was yearning for him to text me.

I just couldn't believe that my husband had cheated on me. I thought the marriage was good, along with money, sex and life were excellent.

I loved him and wanted to save the marriage.

When we went to see the marriage counselor, he said, "I know that she loves me and she's not going anywhere!"

What does that mean? How does he know that I love him, yet he is cheating? I am puzzled by it all!

So, because I am faithful to my vows, he is cheating? He knows that I am not going anywhere, so that means he needs to cheat? Then he said he knows that I'm a good woman! Well, what makes me a good woman? Because I have stuck with him after he cheated?

Didn't he know that I was a good woman before he cheated? He needed to cheat to find out that I am a good woman? I just don't understand his thinking.

JANICE HYLTON-THOMPSON

How Many Chances?

*W*hy do people confuse chances with forgiveness? I believe that my husband has cheated our entire marriage. We have had issues over the years with him cheating, and a woman's intuition is never wrong. Oh yeah, and the condom wrapper in his pocket didn't magically appear.

Looking back, I should have gone to counseling right then and there, but I was crazy in love and gave him another chance. Unfortunately, seven years and many opportunities later, I'm beginning to wonder how many chances do I need to give him? Honestly, I have run out of chances.

This last incident took the cake, with the side chick sending me screenshots of their text messages and pictures of them in a hotel room with her in one of his shirts. To try and save my marriage, I found a Christian marriage counselor.

I told the counselor that I was done and was leaving my husband. The counselor said that if I forgave him, then I wouldn't want to leave. I was taken aback by this comment.

So, my question is: Does forgiveness equal chances? I have forgiven him time and time again and taken him back every time. Now I'm honestly tired, out of chances, and ready to be over with this marriage and move on with my life. Does forgiveness equal chances? Why should I stay with a husband who doesn't want to be faithful? What about me?

I Love My Husband's Mistresses

I don't know what these wives are crying and complaining about. I love the women my husband messes around with.

My love for him went out of the window a long time ago I guess. And I suppose I'm staying for the money at this point. Got tired of crying, begging him to love me, to be faithful, and a good husband. One morning, I woke up and it was as if it didn't matter anymore.

I struggled to get by in life and put myself through school. Always dreamed about the little house with the white picket fence, 2.5 kids, and a dog. I have all of that, and I'm not going to allow some woman to mess that up for my children and me.

We have savings, IRA, investments, health and life insurance. We live in a beautiful house, I have all the clothes, shoes, pocketbooks and some money, and I'm good. I cook for the kids, and I have a maid service that comes once a week to wash and clean my house.

I want my sorry excuse for a husband to be comfortable, so I fixed up the downstairs office and converted it into a man cave with a nice size room, and bathroom. He stays down there, the kids get to see him, and he helps with them. The kids, I, he, and his mistresses are happy. We are one big happy family; what is there to complain about?

And I don't have to fulfill his sexual fantasies with his teeny, tiny "manhood." That's a plus for me!!

JANICE HYLTON-THOMPSON

Who Destroyed Our Family?

hy is there such a double standard when it comes to men and women? He cheats, but I should excuse it because men will be men and I'm supposed to stay and work it out? But when I'm ready to move on because the marriage vows have been broken, I'm being looked down on and blamed for destroying my family? But wait a minute! I didn't cheat! While he was out being a playboy, I was home waiting for him, taking care of our kids, and being a good Christian wife.

Why is it not okay for me to not want to stay in my marriage after my husband has been unfaithful? I want to leave, I don't want to stay, and I don't want to save the marriage. I don't want to go for counseling; I'm done. This is my feeling about this whole cheating thing. He asked me to marry him; I didn't ask him to marry me. So, when we stood in front of God, the Bishop, and all our friends and family, and took those vows to forsake all others, I believed him. That was him telling the world that he wanted me and only me.

When he cheated, that was him letting me know that he no longer wants me and our marriage! I am not about to sit with the Bishop or waste money to sit for hours to talk to a counselor about saving our marriage when this grown man went and laid with someone else.

Then Bishop is upset with me? I am disgusted! I wasn't the one who broke our marriage vows; he did. Be mad at him; be upset with him, but not me. He was the one who entertained this woman. Gave her his number, texted her, spoke to her on the phone, took the time to develop a relationship, took her out on dates, met her at the hotel, and slept with her. He did that!

And now I'm supposed to run to the counselor to try and save my marriage? No, ma'am! It's over! I don't care who survives after adultery, or who works it out. To me, once you have cheated, the marriage is over. The trust is broken, my respect for him is gone, and I can't stand being in the same house with him. The sight of him makes my stomach turn! I can't even look at him anymore!

And this is the man I'm supposed to honor, respect, and submit to? Not me! And you know what else is over? Me going to that church. The same attitude he had towards our marriage is the same one I'm having. He was willing to throw everything away, well so am I! The nerve of Bishop Watermelon! Boy bye!! I'm ready to sign those papers!

Accept It?

*I*t is a known fact that men of a certain nationality cheat. Our elders tell us women point blank that our husbands will cheat because they must have several women. I told them that, that is not acceptable to me. Before I accepted my fiancé's proposal, I explained to him that I believe in monogamy and that if he knew that he could not be faithful to me, then I will not accept his proposal.

While in counseling in front of Father, our elders, and our parents, once again I expressed to him and the elders that if he cheated, I would leave. I have set my standards, and that's it. After four years of marriage, and while I was six months pregnant, I found out that he messed around with an ex-girlfriend.

I started to pack up my stuff while I confronted him. Do you know what he said? He laughed and said, "Don't be stupid. You're not going anywhere. Why would you leave me for foolishness?"

I requested an Uber and checked into a hostel for about a month. Did I mention I was six months pregnant? Our whole family and church were in an uproar. People blocked me on FB and talked about me like I was a dog! My family disowned me and called me everything under the sun but a child of God, and demanded that I return home to my husband.

I finally found a budget-friendly apartment and bought some secondhand furniture. I took a 10K loan from my job pension so that I could be okay while on maternity leave. Plus, I had the money I was saving. I refused to put up with a cheating husband. I saw how my father's infidelity had affected my mother and how she slowly died on the inside. I will not have it!

And if he and our family don't adjust their attitude, they will never see my son! I don't even trust my mother at this point because my Dad has her under his thumb.

And they are always so quick to say that I am too Americanized. No! I know my worth, I deserve better, and I have already set the standard of what I will accept and what I will not. My husband being unfaithful is not acceptable to me, and I will not have it. Wives need to stop accepting that! Men continue to act like little boys because we allow them to! Not me!

Second Chances?

*M*y motto is "You cheat; I divorce you!" I do not believe in second chances when it comes to adultery because my vows did not include cheating! He cheated, and I divorced him. He asked my dad for my hand in marriage. He went and got my Pastor's blessings. We stood before God, our family, and friends, and took vows to forsake all others. And then you are going to cheat and lie about it? Oh, no!

No, we don't need to go for counseling. My feeling is that you should have called a counselor when you were talking, texting and meeting her. Now that you got caught and I went to see my lawyer, you want to go for counseling? Goodbye!

I have seen the sisters in my church put up with that cheating mess, and I have promised myself that, that's something I will never put up with. My motto is "He cheats, and I divorce him." I don't care what people, the church, pastor, or my momma says! There's a cause and effect. When he cheated, it caused me to file for divorce. Seems fair to me!

If he was not ready to commit to being in a monogamous relationship for the rest of his life with me, he should not have married me. Some people were like, "Oh, you need to give him time to get it together!" Time? He had forty-five years to get it together. He is almost fifty, and he still needs more time to get "it" together?

I agree. Let me give him all the time he needs!

Change for Me

Acceptance

*Y*ou always hear that a woman cannot change a man and I agree. However, we all need to make a conscious decision to change when we are in a marriage.

It has been about a year since my divorce, and I have come to accept some of the burdens of the failure of my marriage. My burden is me marrying him knowing that I should not have married him. There were some red flags that I chose to ignore, even though I did talk to him about them. I was hoping that he would change. Ouch, that admission hurts!

I realize now that I cannot change anyone. If he doesn't want to change for himself and God, how can I expect him to change to make our marriage work?

Love Me as I Am

*W*here do I begin? I'm not a petite woman, and my husband knew that when we met, dated, and got married. I'm also not one of those women who like to work out or go to the gym, and yes, he knew that. I hate exercising! I hate the thought of it, and I even hate walking to lose weight. I'm happy with being me, comfortable with who I am, and he said he was too.

So why now, after a year of marriage, is he saying that I need to lose weight and watch what I eat? Gosh, if I could scream, I would! Why can't he just love me as I am? Why can't he take me as I am? This is so not fair to me!

What You See Is What You Get!

*T*he person you meet, date, and marry is the person you will have for the rest of your relationship. If he's obese when you met him and he's not doing anything to be healthier, guess what, he will be that way for the entirety of the marriage! Except if something devastating happens with his health, and then he might be forced to make a change.

If he hasn't been to the doctor in 10 years and tells you once you get married he will go, don't believe him. He's not going to go. If he wasn't going to the gym when you met, and he says he will go once you're married, that's a lie. Who you see is who you have.

If he's in debt and hasn't worked on it while he is single, but says he will see once you get married, that's a lie too. Who you see is what you have. If he's not a communicator when you're dating, guess what? He won't be one when you get married.

If he can't pick up the phone and call and text you throughout the day just to check on you, guess what? What you see is what you will have! If he's cheating on you while you're dating and engaged, guess what, that is what you will have while you're married! You know that old saying "You can't teach an old dog new tricks"? Believe it, it's true!

The person you see in front of you is the one you will marry and have for the rest of your marriage. Unless they make a conscious decision to work to be better for themselves first and then for you.

After 22 years of marriage, I have finally realized that. It was as if a light came on for me. He will not change! So, I will need to either live with it or leave it! Live with what I have been living with for 25 years and be miserable, frustrated, irritated, or leave and get some peace and joy.

Death to Death

*W*hen my marriage died, I died and so did my relationship with God. I don't think people understand that when a marriage dies, it is like a real death, especially if you still love your mate. To say I was shocked and hurt would be an understatement. I stopped praying, reading my Bible, going to Church, fellowshipping and so on. I just kept thinking about our wedding day and how beautiful that day was. Eight years later, people were still talking about how beautiful and happy we both were and what a lovely couple we made.

He just gave up on our marriage and us. He didn't want to be married anymore. I hung on as long as I could. I even went to counseling, but nothing helped to save our marriage. I carried on with our marriage as long as I could, but a marriage takes two people to make it work.

I was mad, angry, bitter, and resentful towards God because marriage is the one thing that I had wanted more than anything else in this world. I was so disappointed in God that depression took over my life. Anger and bitterness moved into my heart as I pushed God out. Coming up in the Church we are taught to wait on God. That we should trust the Lord, save yourself for your mate, serve the Lord, and believe that the Lord will bless you.

I did everything right. I lived my whole life for God. When I was single, every time the doors of the Church opened, I was there serving in whatever capacity I could. When the other young ladies where having boyfriends and babies, I refused to date someone who didn't want to get married. And then, finally, the Lord came through for me, and I met who I thought was my Mr. Forever. Only to get married to have him give up on us, our marriage, our dreams, and our plans?

Sometimes, I think he only married me to have sex with me, because I was adamant about waiting till marriage to have sex. Perhaps that was it? He just wanted to have sex with me? He didn't want me; he just wanted my body? And then he stopped having sex with me because I wanted to have children. He said that it didn't make sense for us to have kids if the marriage was not going to work out.

So, am I mad at God? Yes, I was and still am, to be honest. I have come a long way though. I've been to Church at least twice in the last year. I am wondering if I was supposed to be single. Maybe I'm one of those women who isn't meant to get married and have children like Hannah in the New Testament? But I just can't make peace with being single forever.

I am not at the place of wanting to date or even to go out. I am still sad and depressed about my marriage not working out, and I don't want to be bothered momentarily. I am still so mad, angry, bitter, and resentful about my marriage not working out that I feel as if I can't go on.

Nurse or Purse

*M*y father was a man who had a presence. When he walked into a room, his presence commanded attention — God rest his soul. And when I met my husband, he reminded me of my Dad. You've heard the saying, 'All little girls want to marry a man like their father.' That was true for me. But, I lost my Dad to cancer when I was 16 years old. It broke my heart; I was devastated for years.

I dated here and there, and through college, but I was mainly busy with the family business. Neither Momma nor my brother had a knack for it, but because I love my Daddy so much, I kept it going. It was successful until we decided to sell and made a lovely profit.

Met my husband at a dinner party at a family friend's home. When he walked into the room, his presence commanded attention. He reminded me of my Dad, only shorter. We chit chatted the whole evening and exchanged contact information. Later, we had dinner at the cutest little tavern on the water.

I introduced him to momma, and she said, "Baby, be careful. In Australia, we have a saying that a man like that is looking for a purse or a nurse."

"Nonsense, Mommy! He already has his own money and seems to be healthy and energetic. Plus, you have taught me never to date or marry a poor man!"

Six months later, we were married, and I must admit, it was a bit rushed. Our issues began on our wedding night itself! He was just huffing and puffing and sounded as if he was going to have a heart attack. I was afraid I was going to kill that poor man.

He pooped all night, stayed in the bathroom for hours at a time, ran to the bathroom all the time. I was so grossed out that I couldn't remain in the same room with him. I saw what my Mom was talking about. This man was looking for a nurse to take care of him and clean up his pee and poop.

THE NAKED WIFE

When we were out and about, he was the nicest guy, very attentive and everything a young woman would want in a man.

But that is the problem, I am a young woman, and he is an old man. I am in my 30s and not prepared to take care of a man that is in his 50s. Sorry! I want to enjoy who I'm with, not be concerned if he is going to poop on me while I sleep. Not having to clean up his poop and pee because he couldn't get to the bathroom quick enough.

I want to be able to have sex and have good sex, for hours at a time. I want to be able to run around naked and enjoy my mate. I had a friend that said that in her culture they had a saying — 'Old men have worms.' Beware, young ladies, its true! I realize that my mom was right. I am not ready for the responsibility of an older man. Mom also said I have Daddy issues!

Build a Man

*W*hy did I listen to my Daddy? He told me that I had to make a man for me. Worst advice ever! I need to get him to exercise, eat healthy, go to the dentist, go to the doctor, and keep a job!? It sounds like I was raising a man-child. I think I married a child in a man's body! He reminds me so much of my little brother when we were growing up. And at 33 years old, my Mom is still making excuses for him.

But what if he doesn't become what I want him to be? Then what? Personally, other than a mom raising her baby boy to be a man, I do not believe a wife should take on the responsibility of raising her husband because he is a child. That just seems toxic and stressful to me. The interesting thing is that women are told that we cannot raise our sons to become a man because they need a man to show them how to be a man.

So, how do we as women get with a male who is not a man and try to raise him to be a man for us? That just doesn't make sense. Every day, people tell us to give a brotha a chance. That they are down on their luck and need someone to believe in them. When does it end? Do they ever grow up and become the man that a woman needs so that we can sit back and relax?

You build them, and then they turn around, and you're not good enough for them anymore. They get up and leave us and marry someone else after we build and invest in them. I don't want a man that I have to build. I want a man prepared by God just for me.

Timeout for this "he has potential" mess! He has potential, but I also can meet a man prepared just for me. So, I think I am going to wait for the man made for me!

Children

JANICE HYLTON-THOMPSON

That Was My Clock

I have searched my heart and mind as to why I would marry a man who wasn't my type? He is the kind of man that I would never marry, yet I married him. I have concluded that I was desperate and that this decision was entirely because my clock was ticking. I wanted children and made that very clear while dating, being engaged, and during marriage counseling. But then I came to find out that he didn't even want to have children because of his age. I was 40, and he was 54.

Anyways, I did eventually get pregnant, and I realize now that our marriage changed when it was time for us to start working on having kids. I had so much resentment towards him, but now I am trying to focus on my baby and enjoy her. Isabella is now five years old and just a darling! I can't see my life without her.

Guess that's the price I must pay for marrying an old man who already had children and who just wanted to have a pretty young thang on his arm, but not have any babies or do the work that is required to keep a marriage going. At my age, I really can't deal with inadequacies, foolishness, and bull crap! And please don't get me started on the erectile dysfunction!

Afraid and Insecure

I can see why some couples stay in bad marriages for the kids. My kids love their Daddy, and he loves them. But he refuses to work with me to make the marriage work. So, what do I do? We've been living like roommates for almost four years now.

I have been staying in a marriage that is dead, over, broken, and unfixable, even though I want to try and save it. I told myself that I was staying for the kids, but I think deep down I stayed because I had given up.

He gave up on me, us, and our family. The love and hope I had in my marriage died because I had given him my all. I was afraid to admit that I wanted and deserved better. However, as much as I know how much I deserve and know my worth, I was too insecure to believe that I could have better!

For years, I prayed that he would change, but I now realize that I need to change. Change for my kids and me.

I loved him so much; just wanted to please him and make him happy. But nothing I did was good enough for him. I loved him, but he didn't love our family or me.

No Sacrifice

When I met my husband, I knew that he had a child and I had two. My daughter and I have the custody of my nephew. My kids are well-behaved, straight 'A' students and attend private school their whole lives. I have always lived in an upper-middle-class community because I didn't want my kids to be around the deficiency of the inner cities.

We had one child together, a little boy. Except for everyday couple disagreements, things were going very well.

His son was living with his mother and her new husband but seemed as if he acted out a lot. He was old enough to decide if he wanted to come and spend time with my husband, but he refused. However, he would come by occasionally.

At eighteen years old, he got in some trouble with gangs and was incarcerated. My husband wanted him to come and live with us. I adamantly said no! I didn't want that mess around my kids—not going to school, pants down his behind, hanging out with gangs, and so on. Not around my kids, I'm not having it!

My daughter is a sophomore, my son is in the 8th grade, and our baby is ten. Do you want to bring that foolishness around my kids? I don't think so. Find another way, but he can't live here.

I came home one day and who was in my living room with his stuff in the guest room? His son!

I gladly packed up some things, took the kids, and went to a hotel. I'm not sacrificing my kids and exposing them to the thug and street lifestyle. I don't want that thug around my boys to influence them, and God knows I don't want him around my Princess!

I Stayed for the Kids

I'm not sure if staying in a marriage for the sake of the children, when you know it is over is a good or bad idea. I stayed for my kids and once they all left for college, so did he. Now I'm looking at myself and thinking that I wasted all that time staying under the same roof as my husband, but I honestly cannot say it benefited the children.

Well, they could see him every day, but that's it. We didn't eat as a family; he did stuff with the kids, I did stuff with the kids separately, and the only time we did anything together was at my son's basketball games and the girls' dancing recitals. The only time we were together as a family was for the sole purpose of the children.

I overheard my kids talking one day, and they all said I was stupid for staying with their father. I was so embarrassed! My daughter said she wouldn't do anything that stupid. My son said he didn't want to be like his father, and my other daughter said she didn't want to be anything like me. The sad thing is I did it for them, and now they think I'm stupid.

JANICE HYLTON-THOMPSON

Do Not Hit My Child

*W*e both had children from previous relationships. While dating and being engaged, I made it clear to him that he should not hit my son. His daughter comes over on weekends or whenever the mom wants to drop her off. My son goes with his dad whenever he wants to or when his dad wants to pick him up. Honestly, he spends more time at his Dad's house than at my house.

One-day hubby and I were arguing, and I hate to argue when the kids are there. My son yelled at him not to yell at me. My husband called my son the 'N-word' and my son said, "I am not a "N Word" don't call me that."

He grabbed my son and slapped him. While he was doing that, I was pulling him away from my son. He then pushed my son, and he fell on the floor. I jumped on his back and bit him on the shoulder. I punched him and kicked him so hard you would have thought that I was a boxer.

I do not want him hitting my son, and I have asked that we not argue when the children are there. My son is twelve, and he feels as if he needs to defend me.

Now I know a lot of people will say — 'Oh, he lives there and your husband is taking care of him! Therefore, he should be able to discipline him!' Since people always want to talk about how the stepparent is providing for the child, so he should be able to discipline him, let's get a few things straight. Firstly, my ex-pays good child support, almost $1500 per month. Our mortgage/rent is $1300 because we share with my husband's mother.

So, before people talk, calculate that! My son is bringing in a lot of money in this household. No, all of it doesn't go towards his expenses and needs, some go towards college, savings for him, and some towards expenses. I carry the whole family on my health insurance. I don't want my husband hitting my son!

A Living Sacrifice

*M*y marriage was over before I got married. After we got married, I found out that my husband had slept with his ex the night before we got married. And she sent me the pictures to prove it. I forgave him and hadn't mentioned it. Deep down, I was hurt and disappointed, and the proof is that eight years later, I still haven't printed our wedding pictures.

While I was pregnant, he cheated again, and I was devastated. The Lord blessed me with twins because I'm sure he knew I wouldn't dare sleep with my cheating possibly-STD-infected husband again. When the twins were about one, there was a possible incident, and I moved out. He said he would go to counseling, but he only went to three sessions. I have gone to one with him.

When the twins were almost three years old, I went to see my lawyer and drew up the paperwork, brought our tax returns, paystubs, etc. The lawyer calculated what my child support and possible alimony would be because he made twice what I made.

Can I tell you this man makes me sick? Just the thought of him makes me want to throw up. I hate how he married me, knowing well that he could not be faithful to our vows.

But the way he is with the twins puts a smile on my face. He plays with them, reads stories, gets on the floor, spends an hour in the bathroom giving them baths, dresses them, you name it; he does it for the twins. I have thought about it long and hard and decided that I don't want my children to miss out on the relationship with their Dad, so I have decided to stay for now.

As far as he and I are concerned, the marriage is over. We sleep in separate rooms, and I'm sure he is still messing around. He is a terrible husband, but he is a fantastic father. So, I am sacrificing me for my children.

JANICE HYLTON-THOMPSON

Give Me Children, or Else I Will Die

One of my favorite stories in the Bible is that of Rachel and Jacob, though it's also one of the saddest. Rachel wanted children but was barren, while her sister Leah kept having baby after baby. I feel like Rachel to some extent, because I want to have children, but he doesn't. We were college sweethearts, and he said we were not ready to have kids. "Once you complete your masters," he would say.

Then he encouraged me to get my Ph.D., and then it was, "Oh, our life is perfect without children."

I have done everything including counseling, to try and convince him to have children. Now, I'm forty-five and no kids. No little feet are pitter-pattering around the house, no sending children off to college, none of that.

I resent my husband for that. I wanted children, and I stayed with him hoping that he would change his mind, and now I'm pre-menopausal and no kids. I really shouldn't have stayed with him. This is so sad!

At this point, we don't even talk to each other anymore. We have been married for twenty-three years, and now I am thinking I just wasted my life with this man, waiting for him to decide to have children. The least he could have done was, to be honest with me and tell me that he didn't want to have children, but to allow me to sit here and let my child-bearing years pass me by? That is just sinful!

Infertility

or some reason, the women in my family have a hard time conceiving. I made that known to my husband while we were dating, and he said he was okay with it and that we would try. Five years later, and still no babies. Went to the doctor and the results are that I was not able to have children.

We have tried everything, exhausted our savings to try to get pregnant. Still nothing! I mentioned adoption, but he said no; he wanted his own children. It broke my heart that I was not able to give him children. And it saddens me more that I am not able to birth my children.

At dinner one night, he told me that a young lady was pregnant by him and that he was moving out to be with her and their child. Tears welled up in my eyes, and my heart sank. Even though I was heartbroken, I understood. Then he said he had filed for divorce because he didn't want his child to be born out of wedlock and he wanted to marry the Mom.

Words cannot express the pain and betrayal I felt. I just sat there and cried until I had no tears left.

Why I Stayed

I have every right legally and Biblically to leave my husband. I have even put him out a few times and allowed him to come back, even though I can't stand the sight of him.

I decided to stay under the safe room with him because of my children. We are married on paper, but that's it. We don't have sex, we hardly communicate except for the kids, and all our accounts are set for direct deposit, and the bills are automated, so there is nothing for us to talk about.

I can't stand him. I don't love him. And he has done so much crap to me that it is only because of the grace and mercies of God that I don't hate him. I feel as if he has stolen my life and I wasted it away, waiting for him to keep his ding-a-ling in his pants. I knew the marriage was over when I felt like pushing him down the stairs. I walked up behind him with my hands stretched out. Thankfully, our son called for me. I was so scared, I locked myself in the bedroom and went to see a counselor.

I was planning to leave him. I was in the process of signing a lease to a beautiful two-bedroom apartment for the kids and myself. One morning around 4 a.m., Noah, our baby who was about four years old, woke up and wanted to go to the bathroom. I told him that I would take him, and he cried and said no. He wanted daddy to take him because daddy showed him how to hold his penis.

I was devastated! This was during one of his cheating escapades that I had kicked him out over, and he was out of the house for about a month. I allowed him to come by on the weekends only. This was on a Thursday morning, and so thankfully daddy would come over on Friday evening.

When he came, I told him that he could stay if he wanted to and that we needed to come up with a plan for the kids. I also told him that he could stay downstairs in the living room because he was not allowed in my bedroom.

I can't say that I have forgiven him all the way for how he treated me and how he cheated and lied. But, I realized that morning when Noah was crying for daddy that the kids needed him. So, because of the kids, I am sacrificing myself and my life, so that they can have their daddy under the same roof with them.

The Truth

*C*an I be honest with you? After years of being in this mess of a marriage, I have questioned myself repeatedly about why I married this man. I didn't need anyone to provide for me. I have a Master's degree, an excellent job as a teacher, own my own home, and have my own money.

So why did I marry this man? He is a nice guy, but he is not a nice guy for me. I was thinking the other day that we don't even talk. We never actually talked. We dated for about two years, and when we would go out for dinner, the conversation would be okay.

Then we got married, and we became like strangers. It was as if we are just roommates. I realized that I didn't even like him. Didn't like being around him, being in the same room with him, I didn't like him. So why did I marry him?

The truth is I married him because I was desperate. One day, while walking outside during recess, I was staring at this beautiful tree in the back of the school. It just came to me that while I thought I was secure in being single and waiting on God, I was anxious and desperate. I wanted God-ordained companionship, to be married, and to have children. Being around kids all day didn't help either. But I wasn't meeting anyone.

We are now married, but instead of the God-ordained companionship, I have a grumpy old man as a roommate, passing gas and burping all over the place like he is a child. The thought of him disgusts me! I am so glad that I got pregnant a few months after we got married because if I hadn't, I probably wouldn't have had any kids with him.

Half the time, I don't even know where he is, and I don't care. I'm only staying for my little girl who worships and adores him. I'm not exactly sure what she sees in him, but yeah, that's my story! Sad, right?

Nigger Babies

I am African-American, and my husband is white. We dated on and off in college and finally got married. His Mom and most of his family didn't come to the wedding, which I thought was odd. When I asked him, he said they just couldn't make it, and that his mother was sick. Fast forward five years and I was ready to have children. We had both obtained our masters and were doing well financially. He said he wasn't ready, plus his Mom was sickly, and he was going to have her move here with us, so he could care for her.

Firstly, he should have had the respect and courtesy to have that conversation with me beforehand. But to try and keep the peace in my house, I left it. Plus, I knew I would be the one caring for her because he is lazy around the house. She moved in and, of course, I was the one who took care of all her needs.

Two years later, on my thirty-third birthday, I brought up the conversation to him again about having children. I kid you not, my husband turned red in the face, and his Mom choked on her soup. It was as if they had both seen a ghost. I brushed it off and decided to talk some more about it later.

The next morning, I went for my usual run and returned home through the back door. I overheard my husband's mother telling him that he better not have any 'nigger babies' with that nigger!

"Yes, ma'am," he responded!

"We don't need any more niggers running around here; I don't know why you married her anyway!"

I froze in the kitchen! I wanted to run in the living room to let them know that I had heard them, but for some reason, my legs wouldn't move!

I turned around, went back through the door, and went back to the park, and cried for what seemed like forever! I came home a few hours later and laid down for the rest of the day.

The next morning, instead of making breakfast, I started packing. They were both sitting in the dining room talking and laughing when I came down with my suitcase.

"When are you going to make breakfast and where are you going?" he asked.

With a smile on my face and my head held high, I said, "You mean you want this little 'nigger' to make you some breakfast?"

They both turned pale as I walked out the door and said, "I'm going to find someone who wants to have little 'nagger' babies with me!"

Mixed Babies

I am Italian, but I do not like Italian men. I love black men! I can't explain it, not exactly sure when it happened, but I love black men. In college, I met my Black King. His mother despised me!

"He ain't gonna marry you!" she would often say. "I want beautiful little black grandbabies running around my house, not mixed ones!"

I didn't pay her any mind, and by the time we graduated he hadn't asked me to marry him, so I asked him to marry me. Yes, ma'am! I went and bought myself a ring and got down on one knee and asked him to marry me.

"You're just after his money!" she said.

We went to Las Vegas and eloped. She was pissed and didn't talk to us for about a year. She swears that we are going to get a divorce and I just laugh at her.

We have two little-mixed kids, and she has never come down here to see them. When we fly up to Pennsylvania, nine out of ten times, she isn't available.

I'm starting to feel some resentment from my husband. We had a huge fight a few months back, and he said that I was the reason why he and his mother don't have a relationship and that he hates me for that.

Honestly, I don't care; I am here to stay! I love my husband and our family, and I don't care what his mother says! I'm not leaving! And God knows he has done a lot of things to make me leave, but why should I? Oh, honey that would only make his momma happy!

JANICE HYLTON-THOMPSON

Communication

A Personal Note from Author-Janice

J decided not to include stories on communication because I think in everything we do, we are communicating. Every story in this book, each person is communicating something via their words, actions, and behavior.

To a wife whose husband is abusive, he is communicating fear, anger, death, and hatred.

To a wife whose husband has been unfaithful, his actions say to her that he doesn't love her, she is not enough, she needs to be someone else, and his needs and desires are more important than the needs of her and their family.

To a wife whose husband doesn't want children, but marries her pretending that he wants children, he is communicating that he is a deceiver, a fraud, and a liar.

To a wife, whose husband's penis doesn't work but he marries her under false pretenses he puts his character, integrity, and manhood on trial. And, his actions, says he didn't trust her to put all of his cards on the table. Because just maybe, she wouldn't have chosen him if she knew he has an issue.

To a wife, whom God created with the innate need for a husband to provide for her, when he belittles or abuses her because she doesn't make enough or can't pay half of the bills, it communicates to her that he doesn't know his purpose and she is not worth him providing for her.

To a wife who marries a man because she saw some potential in him, but then he doesn't fulfill it, it says to her that she made a mistake, that he made her believe a lie.

To a wife whose husband doesn't love her for who she is, it says to her that she is not enough, and if she would only change 'this' about her, then and only then will she be good enough for him.

Everything we do, we are communicating something; so be careful what your actions say about you.

JANICE HYLTON-THOMPSON

Conflicts

The Ultimate Ultimatum

*F*ell in love and eloped with my college sweetheart. Eloped, because I knew my parents would not go for me marrying a man who was not a born-again believer and who did not believe that Jesus Christ is the Son of the living God. Now that I think about it, I was in rebellion against my parents and the Church.

When he asked me out, I knew I should not have accepted. Every step of the way, I knew I was wrong. It was as if that little voice on the inside was saying, "You know what you were taught." When I went to his religious organization with him, and I had to cover up and sit with the women, it was as if God was standing up inside of me saying, "No, no, no."

Later, I told my parents, and it broke their hearts, but they said they would be praying for me. They showed me grace by continuing to pay for my college education. Every Friday Daddy would put money in my account. They'd invite my husband and me to come over, but he never wanted to go because my Daddy is a preacher.

While we were in college, it was good because we were so busy with classes. Once we graduated and started to live in the real world, our issues started. He tried daily to convert me. He invited the women and men from his religious organization to seek to convert me.

I noticed that the 'still little voice' inside me was getting weaker and weaker. But every time I spoke to Mommy and Daddy, they would tell me about Jesus. Even though I was working, Daddy was still putting money in my account and telling me about my room still at the house.

One day, we got into a big fight because he was ready to have children and I wasn't. I honestly couldn't bring myself to have kids in this situation because I remember being in Sunday School as a child. Those were some of my fondest memories.

During our fight, he yelled, "Reject Jesus and convert or get out of my house!"

Suddenly, my whole life flashed before my eyes. Hell flashed before me, and I yelled, "Kill me if you must, but I will never reject Jesus because Jesus Christ is the Son of God!" I grabbed my purse, ran out and haven't looked back. I am so thankful to God for my daddy who drove all night to come and pick me up.

God knew what He was saying when He said we should not marry unbelievers.

Double-minded

*T*here's such conflict within me! What does the Bible say? "A double-minded man is unstable in all his ways." Yes! That's me! I am double-minded. Today I love him, but tomorrow I will hate and resent him.

Today I want to have his baby, but tomorrow I will want to tie my tubes. Today, I want us to make passionate love, but tomorrow I don't want him to even look at me.

Today I want to stay married, but tomorrow I will want a divorce. I have Biblical reasons to divorce him.

Today he's the perfect gentleman, but tomorrow he will act like such a jerk. I need to decide what I am going to do. We can't continue to live like this.

Conflict Within

I can honestly say I love my husband. I can honestly say that at this moment, I do not want anyone else. I know that I like having him in the house, but when he's away, his absence gives me great peace.

What I cannot say is that I am ready to fight for this marriage. Be it in prayer, fasting, or faith.

I am honestly tired! Tired of fighting and quarreling, tired of the loveless marriage, tired of the sarcasm, and since we haven't been having sex, I'm sure he has it somewhere else. I'm just over him and this marriage!

Mr. Perfect?

*I*t's the strangest thing I have ever seen. My husband doesn't like me to say I don't like something. It got so bad that just telling him that I didn't like his mother to just show up at our home and that I would appreciate it if she called ahead of time, meant that I had to schedule an appointment with our counselor. And I mean, it's with everything now. I feel as if I can't say anything to him about anything.

I don't usually drink coffee, but he is a big coffee-drinker. Some mornings, I would make coffee, and notice he didn't drink it. One morning, I asked if he wanted some coffee and he said no. So, I asked him if something was wrong with it, and if so, to tell me so I could fix it. He said, "No, nothing is wrong with it." An hour later, he made another pot of coffee.

I said to him, "See, if I had done that, you would have had a tantrum! I am okay with you telling me how you like your coffee."

I do believe that he thought he was perfect. That was why our marriage was in trouble because he thought he was perfect and he could do no wrong. I had to move out for a whole month before he went for counseling! He never apologized for anything! If he did, it was done sarcastically. And then, he started talking about having children? Not! There was no way I could build a life and family with him.

In the end, it just didn't work! I got tired of walking on eggshells and not being able to say a word about anything. I was afraid of even opening my mouth because it would result in a fight. It was as if I was in a play where I needed to pretend that everything was perfect.

My parents have been married for over thirty years, and the one thing they always told me then was that I had to work at my marriage. But, it takes work for two people to become one, and we never became one!

Tomorrow Never Comes

*M*y husband never had time for me, wanted to talk, or to discuss anything. Every chance I got, I would try to talk to him, and he would always say, "Baby, let's talk tomorrow." The house, the lawn — "Let's talk tomorrow. The heat, Baby, not now!"

One day, I was outside with the kids, and he came home, and we sat there for about an hour. I started to try to talk to him about stuff. He said, "Baby, why can't we just sit and enjoy the kids? Why do you always want to speak?" But when I take the initiative and get things done around the house, he gets upset? I'm not exactly sure what to do. I suggested counseling, but even to that he says, "Let's talk about it later."

So, I went to see a counselor, and she suggested that we carve out fifteen minutes a day. But how do *I* carve out fifteen minutes a day with someone who doesn't want to talk or go to counseling? I'm not even sure how I got pregnant with these children.

I am starting to realize that I am my husband's midlife crisis mistake. I don't know what made me think that a man that has been a bachelor his whole life would change his life around for me. He never wanted to talk or deal with issues that we were dealing with. We would be in the house the whole day and other than 'good morning,' if I didn't say anything to him, he didn't speak.

Half the time he didn't even want to be bothered with the kids. He was always too tired to play with them, take them to the park, get up early to be up with them, give them baths, etc. He just didn't seem interested at all.

When I brought up these issues, he always said, "Tomorrow, Baby, not today." It was frustrating and irritating! So, I am basically in this marriage alone.

115

A Good Name

I have worked very hard to make a name for myself and provide a comfortable life for my children. There was only one thing that was missing. My husband! Finally, I met a nice guy at a church luncheon. He wasn't the typical guy that I usually date — men of substance who have their own money. Nevertheless, I decided to give it a chance.

About a year and a half after dating, we got married. It lasted ninety days! He wanted me to change my name. We talked about it while we were dating, and he was okay with me hyphenating it. Once we got married, he started saying that I needed to change my name; he was my husband, I needed to submit to him, and that this was not acceptable in the church.

Then he said my name was worthless!

"Wait a minute!" I said. "My name is worthless? Sir, let's compare our names! You couldn't get a house in your name because your credit is so jacked up! I own a beautiful six-bedroom home in my name! I have three kids with my name. I have several businesses in my name. I own properties in my name. I have a Ph.D. in my name; you have a GED! My name is not worthless. At 42 years old, I don't see what's wrong with hyphenating my name."

Then he gave me an ultimatum. Change my name or get out of his house. So, I packed myself and my kids up and moved out of his *little* three-bedroom townhouse that he was renting, and moved back to my *big* six-bedroom house where all my kids have their own rooms. And lots of space outside to run around and play.

Before I walked out, I said, "The Apostle said, if MasterCard, Visa, and American Express don't trust you to put your name on plastic, how you dare want to put your name on a woman? And the Bible says a good name is to be honored."

Strangers

I was walking the aisle of my favorite store, looking at some shirts and ties and thinking, *"Oh this would look lovely on my Daddy."* Suddenly, I realize that after four years of marriage, I feel as if we are still strangers. There is no connection at all between us! I should think that a shirt and tie would look nice on my husband, but I'm not.

We live in a lovely home, but we are like roommates. He stays in his bachelor room, and I hang out in the rest of the house. Whenever mom asks me to host holiday dinners, I say no. When she once forced herself over for my birthday dinner, she said it felt so cold in the house. Ironically, it was 85 degrees outside.

My husband is not a communicator. He doesn't talk, and having a conversation with him is like pulling teeth. He just grunts and shakes his head. When we were dating, I remember talking to him about our communication issues, and he said he would work on it.

It's ironic how that was one of the key factors I used to see if a guy and I were compatible. If they were not able to keep me on the phone for hours, I would drop them because my Mommy always told me that communication was critical.

She and Daddy would stay up late at night for hours talking and laughing. Sometimes I woke up and thought they were having a party, and when I would go down to the basement, it was just the two of them. I wanted that for my marriage.

For my husband, I threw that out and excused him because he was busy working and didn't have much time to talk on the phone. It is so weird that the one thing I overlooked is the thing that has torn us apart. I yearn for conversation and communication as I yearn for air. He hasn't given it to me; he hasn't implemented any of the ideas the marriage counselor suggested, and now I feel as if I have died. I don't even talk to him anymore.

Over time, we have become strangers.

JANICE HYLTON-THOMPSON

The Day I Stopped Loving Him

I remember the day I ceased to love my husband. November 17th, in a snowstorm. I had just given birth to our twins. All through the pregnancy, I insisted that he take the babies' car seats to the police or the fire station so that they could help him put them in.

He refused and insisted that he could do it. Well, came the day when I was supposed to go home with my twins, after staying five days in the hospital. The twins and I were standing outside in the cold, sleet, and snow because the car seat wasn't right.

After about 15 minutes of him struggling with the car seats, I said that I was cold. Who told me to say that? He yelled and screamed at me and cursed me out like I was some whore on the street! Right in front of the hospital. The security guard came over and asked if everything was okay, and walked with the twins back into the hospital lobby. Then he went back and helped my husband with the car seats.

Once the car seats were put in, he didn't even come and get us. The security guard did and asked if I was okay and did I feel safe to go home with him. I told him yes that my mother was home and we would be okay.

All the way home, I cried. And I do not cry easily, but he hurt me! I had just given birth to his children. They had to cut me open. I spent five days in the hospital, and this was the way he treated me?

When I got home, I was glad to see my Mom who asked me why I was crying. I told her I was tired, and she took the twins. I went to bed and, that night, I grabbed my pillow and held it close to me as if I was holding my husband. At that moment, my heart stopped beating for him. That day, my heart closed and left, and it will never open again for him.

"Oh, my body's still here, living under the same roof for my children's sake. But five years later my heart is still gone, and there is no opening for him to reenter!"

The Cost of My Marriage

I'd always wanted to get married, but I ended up marrying the wrong man. The wrong man cost me my fellowship with the Lord. Notice I said fellowship and not a relationship. There's a difference between relationship and fellowship. My relationship is that I will always be His child, but it's been a while since I fellowshipped with Him!

I am so saddened and hurt by my marriage that I have stopped going to church, ceased to pray, and stopped reading my Bible. I don't even want to watch Church TV anymore because I am so distraught. I believed God for my husband and, yes, I know that there is no perfect person out there, and we all need to compromise on some levels.

But I over-compromised and overlooked a million red flags. I often pray and ask the Lord why He didn't tell me not to marry him. But if God told me, would I have listened? As a matter of fact, after spending time thinking about it all, I realize that the Lord did speak. He showed me all the red flags, and I chose to overlook them, over-compromised and ended up with the man I have today.

I married the kind of man I never wanted to marry. I felt as if I have wasted my life and time waiting on God, and now that I'm married, I blame God. I blame God for sending this man, I blame God for not speaking to me and letting me know that this man was not for me.

At the same time, I do have some bitterness towards the Church, because they always tell us, young ladies, to give a man a chance. Compromise some, so what he doesn't have all that you want in a man. Help him to build and build him up to become the husband you want.

Opposites Attract

Opposites attract. I remember my husband said that when he was pursuing me. We are like night and day! It took a long time for me to go out with him because I just didn't think we had anything in common.

He was not my type of guy physically or personality-wise. I'm more athletic, and he's like a coach-potato. That was an instant turn-off for me because I like my man to be physically fit! I'm an extrovert, and he's an introvert. I'm more social, and you have to pull him out of his cocoon.

Finally, I went out with him, and he was a very nice guy. He spoke very well, was hardworking, and a churchman. I liked those characteristics about him. But other than that, there was nothing else about him that I liked. But I said, what the heck, let me give it a chance! We dated, and he would try to impress me by coming to the gym occasionally and walk to the park. But, I still didn't feel any fire or passion for him. There was just something missing.

It took time for me to get to know him. Two years later, we got married and what do you know? — Living in the same space with him, I realize that I can't stand him! It's as if I am living with my brother. He sits around on the weekends in his pajamas and watches TV, and he doesn't even shower! That is so disgusting!

Now when I ask him to go to the park and walk with me, it's as if I cursed at him or something. Or for him to pick up after himself — that turns into a big fight. Honestly, I don't know what I'm going to do with this nonsense! Opposites might attract for some reason, but it will not work if we don't have some glue to keep us together.

You would think faith and a good job would be enough, right?

Dear Husband:
Another Woman's Children

*P*ampers, cribs, strollers, car seat, blankets and teddy bears! So much to buy, so much to prepare for! This should be a happy occasion, but I breathe the breath of sadness, hurt, and pain. This should be my baby, our baby. This is another woman's child that you are expecting me to help you and her to raise. The audacity of it all!

You know what hurts the most? That this is not the first time. This is baby number three that you have fathered outside of our marriage. This newest one you've brought home! For me to nurse, change, and love. How can I do that? How can you expect me to do that? I'm sorry, but I don't have the strength or the grace.

I am afraid that one day you will come home and your baby, her baby, will be nowhere to be found. So, I think it's best for me to go, depart, and remove myself from this situation. You do not have any respect for the vows we took as we stood before God, our pastors, family, and friends almost twenty years ago now.

If I could give you children, I would, but unfortunately, I can't. When I was raped as a teen, that affected my reproductive system. I have asked you if we could adopt, but you refused. "I want my own flesh and blood," was all I have heard from you over the years.

So, I leave you, my dearest husband, with your children and your mistresses. I am sure God will not count me wrong for leaving. How many more adulterous relationships am I supposed to stick with you through? How much can one woman go through with an unfaithful husband who refuses to honor his vows?

You did not honor me in our marriage; I pray that you will honor me in our divorce. The house is mine. I have spent the last twenty years making it my home. Alimony is a must, half of your pension and retirement savings. It's only fair that I get something out of this sham of marriage!

Trapped by The Trapper

I trapped him by getting pregnant, and now I feel trapped because I know he's not happy. And about his extracurricular activities. I'm not sure if I fell in love with the person or with the title of a doctor.

I wanted to make my parents proud because I married a doctor. I know he didn't love me or want to marry me, and so I got pregnant because I knew his story. He was raised in a single-mother home and vowed that his children wouldn't be raised like that. So, I got pregnant, and it took him eight months to marry me, but when I gave birth to our son, I was a married woman.

And when I went back to work after a three-month maternity leave, I was pregnant again.

Three babies later, I know that he can't stand me. When he's home, he spends all of his time with the children. If I don't say anything to him, he doesn't speak.

Sometimes, I want him to love me, want me, desire me, but three babies later, he still doesn't love me. At times, I feel trapped and realize that I deserve better. I deserve to be loved.

So, we are living in this big house that he finally put us in. The kids and I live upstairs, and when he does come home, he stays downstairs in the guest room. When he puts the kids to bed and heads out, I already know what time it is.

But you know what, who cares? We are married, we have children. I drive a nice car. We have food and clothing, shelter, and money in the bank, even though he doesn't put all his pay in the account. But I'm good. At least, I am married to a doctor! Maybe being trapped isn't so bad after all.

I am not going anywhere, and if he decides to leave, at least I will get good child support! Plus, what is the difference between me staying in my marriage and a wife where her husband cheated, and she is trying to work it out?

Tantrum

I was married for six years, and for five years, my husband would have a tantrum at least once, sometimes twice a month, where he would run to his Momma's house. It could be about anything. If I asked him to close the toilet seat, turn the alarm on, ask why the door was unlocked, etc., he would get the huffing and puffing and pack his stuff and run to Momma.

This last time, I had to ask myself why I was putting up with a man-child. Who does that? Where every time I say something you don't like, you throw a tantrum? What grown, fifty-five-year-old man does that? And then, comes back home and acts like nothing happened, like he was on vacation, and I need just to run and jump in his arms because I missed him so much? I was done!

How come I don't have that luxury? I must stay here and take care of these children, drop and pick them up from school and daycare. Our little boy has baseball practice; I must drive him. Our little girl was running in the kitchen and fell and busted her lip and I had to pack all three children up and take them to the emergency room.

When he left for a week, didn't even come by to check on the kids or ask if he can help with them. So, I did him a favor! I packed all his stuff, called a moving truck, and had them deliver all of it to his Momma's house, and then I changed the lock on the door and went to see my lawyer.

I sent him on a permanent vacation to his mother's house, and I made sure the divorce papers were addressed to him in care of his Momma.

Grow to Love Him?

*I*n my culture, your family chooses your mate. I will admit that I wasn't in love with my husband when I married him. I don't even think I liked him. Maybe as a brother in the Lord, but, as far as in love? No. Guess that explains never having any passion for him.

Sex was a chore, felt like rape and torture. Having the baby was a job, and I love my kid, but now I just can't stand my husband. Then he wanted to have six children; it was repulsive. He was way older than me, and the sight of him was sickening. I felt as if I was living for my family and not for me.

Everything about him nauseated me: the way he chewed, brushed his teeth, snored, his big gut, his voice; I despised him. I bought cologne that smelled good on my coworker that I loved, but it stank on him.

In the meantime, the man I loved ended up marrying another because my family thought he wasn't good enough for me. *You'll grow to love him*, my mother often said. But I don't think I will ever love him, and I can't see spending the rest of my life with him.

Deception

Lies

&

Sex

The Celibate Wife

*T*he first thing church folks want to tell you when you are having issues in the bedroom is that sex doesn't matter. Or that there is more to marriage than sex. But when God created Adam and Eve, he told them to be fruitful and to multiply. Adam and Eve were only able to become one when they had sex. Sex was representative of marriage in the Bible. So how does the church tell us that sex doesn't matter?

Many couples have sex before they get married, both in and out of the church. Our churches are filled with unwed mothers with multiple children, but they want to tell married folks that sex doesn't matter?

I was celibate for a long time!! A very, very long time. Finally got married to a minister in the church. There was no sex or attempt of sex on his part while dating and engaged. We got married, and on our wedding night, he tells me that his penis doesn't work at all!!!? I was shocked!

I told him that we could try and see. He said, no that his penis doesn't work period. When I asked him why he didn't tell me that before, guess what he said? He said, "sex doesn't matter if a couple loves each other." I almost screamed!!

The next day I decided to bring it up, and he acted as if he didn't care at all. He then said that he wanted to become an Elder in the church and in his church, you have to be married.

I was so embarrassed that I couldn't believe my ears or have the decency to tell our pastor. After about a month I got the courage to go and talk to Pastor, and guess what Pastor said? "Oh, sister Naomi, sex is overrated. Sex doesn't matter, and there's more to a marriage than sex."

I felt like I was in a prison of shame, embarrassment, and celibacy. To my fault, I stayed in the marriage and even adopted three kids with this fraud!! Five years later, I just couldn't do it anymore. I was tired of being a celibate wife! For five years of marriage, my husband and I have never had sex!!

THE NAKED WIFE

I divorced that fraud, got full custody, alimony, child support and the house. The judge was disgusted with him and said he had to pay me alimony for ten years!! After that, I called my ex-boyfriend who I loved, but he wasn't "spiritual" enough, so I had passed him up for this fraud!! For those five years, I thought that maybe that was God punishing me?

Honestly, I didn't care at that point. I felt anger, disgust, and resentment towards God. And the last thing I was going to do was hold out for another husband or be celibate. I tried it, did everything right and what did I get? A non-working "ding-a-ling" minister for a husband!!

Once I reconnected with my ex, we went away for a whole week, and the rest is "HER-story" You know, I'm still not back in the church as much as I should over that entire situation. Even do to this day, almost three years later, I feel betrayed by God! SMH!!

Traveling Viagra

J was married for almost 14 years. My husband provided, and he was good with the kids. Sex was never his best activity. I just dealt with it because he was a good father. He had been getting Viagra, but honestly, I didn't think it made a difference. Again, I just dealt with his incapability because he was a good man. In my days, a good man is one that works and put food on the table, clothes on our backs and roof over our heads.

One day, I was putting his clothes in his drawer as he was outside picking up the garbage from our lawn. Something told me to check his bag for the Viagra. I checked the Viagra, and it said four on the bottle, but there were only two in there. We hadn't had sex in almost a year because if he didn't initiate, I didn't bother to try.

The prescription was filled three months before, so where were the other two? I didn't make a big deal out of it because one of my favorite scriptures was to be wise as a serpent and yet harmless as a dove. A week later, I rechecked it, and it was in his work bag. Both were gone. I didn't say anything.

A month later, we were going to his family reunion, but he needed to go days ahead to set up. I checked the Viagra, and he had gotten a refill. When he left, there were two in the bottle. When I got there, I checked it, and there was one left. The kids and I spent two days there and came home. He came back two days later. When he returned, the Viagra bottle was empty.

I confronted him without asking about the Viagra, and he denied that he had been cheating. I called a marriage counselor, and he refused to attend at first. When I threatened to put him out, he agreed to go. We went to two sessions without me bringing up the Viagra. In the third meeting, I asked him about his Viagra, and he said they were in his drawer.

I went back to all the time he used the Viagra, got refills, and used them, etc. The last incident was the straw that broke the camel's back. The same bed that his kids and I were coming to sleep with him at his family reunion was the same bed he had screwed someone in. And then, after I confronted him about cheating while he was there, he denied it but came home with an empty bottle?

He was speechless with his mouth hanging wide open! I yelled "In 14 years of marriage and two years of dating, I can count the time on both of my hands I had an orgasm with you, but I was faithful. Eighteen years of bad sex, but I stayed with you because you were a good man. You worked and provided, and the kids and I have never been hungry, homeless or naked, so I stayed with you. I pushed the sex to the side and decided just to be satisfied with what you were able to do since you didn't seem too interested in pleasing me, finding out what I like, and so on."

"I tried to get us to go see a sexologist, and you had a fit and said we didn't need all of that, but I stayed with you, again denying my needs and wants because I thought you were a good man. And you were cheating on me all this time!?

"I want a divorce, alimony, child support, half of your social security and whatever else I can get. I want the house and the truck and half of all the retirement and savings accounts. How dare you when I have put up with you for all these years!"

Why Me?

*W*hy, why, why, and why? Why did I have to be the one that ended up with a down low brotha? In this day and time, I cannot believe that there are still men on the down low. In a time of freedom where everyone and their mommas are coming out of the closet, why in God's name is it that the man I married was still in the closet?

I would have never thought that there were men that were still doing this mess to innocent women! Women, who want to be married and have children? Only to marry the fool and he won't even touch you!

How do you intentionally destroy someone's life because you are trying to hide who you are? If you are a man who likes men, why would you pursue a woman and marry her while sleeping with other men? Let me answer that! That is pure evil, wickedness, deception, and the work of the Devil!

I went to talk to Pastor, and he suggested before I file for divorce, we should try to save the marriage! Let's face it; there are some marriages that CAN'T be saved! How do you counsel out homosexuality? That's an injustice of the church to women who must deal with these snakes that seek cover from vulnerable women to cover up their lifestyle!

My husband is sleeping with men! He was on the DL when we got married and was using me as a cover. There is no counseling for that. I'm not staying with a man who is sleeping with other men!

That's My Sister

When I met my husband, he didn't have his papers. We fell head over heels in love, and in about a year and a half, we got married. Once we got married, we started working on his papers so that he could become a legal resident of the United States. He didn't have a stable job, so I was the breadwinner. He would send money to his sister and son back home in the Islands.

Eventually, he became legal and began the paperwork to bring over his son, who was about thirteen, and his sister. They came to visit us the next summer, and it was nice to meet his family finally. But something was a bit strange about everything. I just couldn't put my finger on it. Anyways, the following week, his son went to Brooklyn to spend some time with his aunt, and that left three of us in the house. I worked during the day, and he worked at night.

One day, as I drove to work, something told me to go back home. At first, I questioned myself, but for some strange reason the whole week I'd felt like I needed to go back home. I made a U-turn, and in forty-five minutes I was pulling up in my parking spot. I turned the key in the door, and all I heard was screaming and yelling, among other expressive terms.

I ran to my bedroom and what did I find? My husband was having sex with his sister! I was shocked, and I ran to the kitchen to get my butcher knife. Came back in the room and went towards my husband. They both ran out of the house butt naked while I chased them down the hallway!

He always left his keys to his truck that I bought him in a tray by the door. So, he grabbed it and whatever they could to cover up. Apparently, that wasn't his sister but his wife from home, and he only married me to get his papers, so he could bring them up here.

Everyone was in on it but me. That is so deceptive. Do you know how often I had spent time with his family? Everyone was in on the secret but me.

Two of Everything

After 25 years of marriage, my husband got sick and went into a coma. I needed to provide a list of people who could visit him. I was home late one night, and my phone rang. It was the hospital calling me that they had an emergency about my husband and I needed to come quickly!

I thought he had taken a turn for the worse. So, I got dressed and arrived at the hospital in 15 minutes. I was shocked to see two teenage boys that looked just like my husband. The same eyes, ears, curly hair, and their birth certificates that he signed. I fainted, and the nurse caught me. I couldn't believe it!

I broke down crying, and the doctor asked if I would let them see their Daddy and I nodded yes. Apparently, his mother and the rest of his family, who never liked me, knew about the kids and hid them from me. It worked because they lived in a neighboring state. His Mom had called them to let them know he was in a coma.

All these years, I thought we had a good marriage. So why does my husband have two of everything? Two kids outside of our marriage? Two houses, two insurance policies, two Wills, two cars, two bank accounts, and apparently there are two of him too because I am still in disbelief that he did this.

Still Not Pregnant

*A*fter trying almost two years to get pregnant and nothing! At first, my doctor said I needed to try a year before she began to run any tests especially since I have been on birth control for some years now.

Finally, we started running tests to see if everything was okay with me. All my tests came back with flying colors! The doctor said it was time to start checking my husband. At first, he hesitated, but after my begging and pleading, eventually, he went. My doctor began to do tests on him and guess what she found?

When the doctor called, she asked him to come into the office. I asked if I needed to come too, and she told me to ask my husband. He then told me that he had a vasectomy a few years back. He didn't tell me before because he thought that I wouldn't marry him.

In all honesty, can you say that I should stay in this marriage? What am I supposed to do? Not have children? Stay with a man who lied and deceived me? How do I lay next to him at night? How do I sit across the dinner table and look at him?

How can I respect him? Do I pray to God to take away my desire to have children? I wasted five years of my life with this demon, making plans for our children, and all the while he couldn't have children.

I went to talk to Pastor, and he spoke about counseling to save the marriage. Counseling? There is nothing to counsel! This marriage can't be saved! How do you save this mess? I was not going to allow him to waste another second of my life!

Decisions, Resolutions & Peace

A Step of Faith

After much soul-searching, praying and crying, I decided to take a step of faith and file for divorce. For years, I stayed in a marriage that was over out of fear. Not because I loved him or wanted to save the marriage, but because I was afraid.

I was fearful for my children, about my finances, and about what my family and friends would say. On the outside, we looked like the perfect little family, but no one knew what was going on, on the inside. The truth is, I was a single parent. We were struggling financially because he was terrible with money, and I was alone. We were married on paper only. We hadn't had sex in over three years. We didn't even sleep in the same bed. We didn't communicate, and we hated to be around each other. So, why was I fighting to save this dysfunction?

I tried to and wanted to save our marriage, but I couldn't do his part for him. I even tried living under the same roof with him, but it was as if it was a war zone. We fought every day and night. There was no peace, not one day where we weren't fighting about something.

I realized that once the love and respect are gone, nothing is left. My love and respect for him were affected the first time I knew he cheated. I forgave him, or at least I said I forgave him, but now I realize that it hurt me more than anything. The second time I knew about it, I was crushed, and I believe I died on the inside.

Honestly, I don't think he ever loved me. How can you hurt someone you say you love so much? How do you continue to cheat and be unfaithful, when I have given him chance after chance to try and save our marriage? I wanted to save our marriage for our children to the point that I would do anything.

But I realized that a peaceful and healthy environment with one parent is better than a violent one where parents don't love and respect each other. It was not good for my kids to hear their father calling me the 'b' word. It was not good for them to hear me calling their father a bastard or a no-

135

good piece of crap. I couldn't stand him, and he couldn't stand me. I think we were at the place where we hated each other. And, honestly, I hated that.

At this point, I am honestly over men. I have been so traumatized by this one that I just want some peace.

My Dearest Husband

*A*s I lay here, my heart is wrapped in pain; my eyes are sore from crying. My mind is running back and forth trying to figure out how you could? How could you treat me this way? How could you be unfaithful to me, to us, to our family, to our vows? You were supposed to be my Mr. Awesome, but instead, you've turned out to be Mr. Terrible! You were supposed to be my knight in shining armor, but instead, you've proved to be a wolf in sheep's clothing!

You know, I think back to the first time we met. Do you remember how we met? It was as if it was divine intervention. I didn't want to come out that night, but another part of me was telling me to go out. "Mingle, meet new people!" my roommates said. "You never know who you might meet the one!" said my cousin.

When I walked in, our eyes met. Your eyes followed me the whole evening until you got enough courage to come and talk to me. It still brings a smile to my face remembering how nervous you were!

I remember you complimented me on my perfume. Do you remember the name of the perfume I was wearing that night? We talked and laughed all night, and then you asked me for my telephone number. I gladly gave it to you on a napkin, and you kissed it. You were the perfect gentleman that night, and you surprised me the next day when you showed up at my church.

After church, we went out and talked until almost midnight. Do you remember how we kept ordering a new meal every three hours so that they wouldn't kick us out? Remember the booth we sat in? That was our spot for years; we would go and wait for it to be available.

That was the place I knew you were unfaithful because you had changed. You didn't look at me the same way you used to. You stopped holding my hands and kissing me on my forehead. That was the place I realized that you didn't love me anymore; and somewhere, somehow, over the 25 years of our marriage, you had lost that soft look in your eyes for me.

I Don't Love Myself

*W*oke up early one Sunday morning and it was as if a light came on. *"I am staying with him because I don't love myself. I have always cared more for him than he did for me."* That epiphany was very hard for me. Me not loving myself? In the beginning, we had a good thing. We made plans, and we got married. We were blessed with two beautiful children and had a beautiful home. We had no bills, had a little money saved up, and we should have been happy, but something was just off with us.

It was later that I found out that my knight in shining armor was unfaithful. It devastated me, and we were separated for six months. He acted as if he was glad to be out of our home. We went to counseling, and then he moved back in, only to find out that he was continuing the adulterous relationship.

My heart just quit, and I sucked it up only for the kids, but deep down I wanted out. It was as if there was a war going on the inside. One day I would think, *"My kids need their father."* And the next day I would think, *"Why settle for this? I am only 35. Surely I am still young enough to meet someone to have a wonderful life with?"*

But five years later, I am still here thinking, wanting to leave, but at the same time wanting for my kids to see their daddy every day. I used to say I wouldn't stay, but now that I have children, I can understand why many women stay with a man who is not doing right by them.

The truth is I don't love myself! I have always loved him more than he loves me. I have always cared for him more than he cared for me. Here I am trying to keep us all under the same roof, but he doesn't even care to be here with us. His behavior and attitude reek with disrespect, and he is so sarcastic! I am concerned about how he will afford child support and an apartment?

He is an official, and I think, *"What are his other council members going to say and think about him?"* But apparently, he doesn't care because if he did, he wouldn't have cheated or he would have tried to save our marriage. So, if he doesn't care, why am I losing sleep worrying about him?

I am worried about the disruption of the relationship between him and the kids, but he just doesn't seem to care at all. The only thing left for me to do is to get on bended knees and beg him to do right by us and try to save our marriage for our children. Why wouldn't he want to save our marriage for our children?

I realize now that I am more concerned about him than I am about myself because I do not love myself. I love him more than I love myself and that's a problem!

Fear

*O*ur marriage has been dead for a very long time! And while we tried to resurrect it for about five years, we just couldn't do it because it was dead. Honestly, I was so sad, depressed, and devastated that my marriage was over that I just gave up. I gave up on life and love. My hope was gone. The death and failure of my marriage even affected my faith in Christ.

How was that possible? My whole life, all I ever wanted was to get married and have children and a family. Then I got married and married a man who was not as committed and did not want a family as much as I did. Oh, he said he was committed and wanted marriage and a family. However, once we got married, it was evident that he was only talking and said what he needed to say to get me to marry him. Unfortunately, I believed him only to realize that it wasn't so.

Do you want to know something sad? Knowing all of this, I stayed with him for ten years! I wanted the marriage to work, and I even had children with this man.

Why did I stay? Simply put, I stayed because I was fearful. I was afraid of my family splitting up; and yet, we didn't have a family at home. I was scared that I would not meet anyone else; and yet, I didn't have a husband. I had a roommate. I was scared of my kids not having a father; and yet, he was not setting good examples for our children.

I was scared for my kids and didn't want another man fathering them, especially my sons; and yet, their dad wasn't fathering them at all. I was afraid of getting into another relationship because the new man might molest my girls. I was afraid to trust God to provide and supply all of our needs because I had believed Him my whole life for a husband, and the husband I got was awful. I was afraid to try to love again because my heart had closed.

I wanted to love and knew that I deserved to be loved, but I was scared for my children. And then, a friend told me to read the story of Job. She explained to me that Job was afraid for his children, but the thing he feared the most, happened to them.

One day, I got up, went for a walk and to have a talk with Jesus about my fears and concerns. Less than 30 days later, I got over my fear and asked him to leave.

It has been three years now, and our divorce is final. This has been the happiest and more fulfilling three years of my life. If you are in fear, you cannot be in faith! Because fear is crippling, but faith is liberating.

JANICE HYLTON-THOMPSON

The Best Thing

The best thing I could have ever done for my marriage was to give up on it. I was so tired of fighting to save it, to keep us together and under one roof that I made myself sick. I was sick and laid up in the hospital for stress.

I asked to see a chaplain, and I told her everything. She looked me straight in my eyes and said, "Let him go and stop fighting!" I cried because I loved my husband and my family so much and I didn't want us to break up, but I was the only one fighting. I was the only one running to the counselor's office. I was the only one being faithful and behaving like a married person.

But, when the doctor wouldn't let me go home, and I had no one to watch my kids, I gave up. I gave up on him, us and the marriage. I decided to focus on the most essential thing in my life, my children and myself.

I stopped caring about him and doing things for him. I ceased to wonder where he was, why he didn't call, what he was looking at online, and who he was talking to on social media.

I started smelling the roses, enjoying my children, going to the gym, hanging out with my friends, or taking a day off from work and going to the spa or a movie. I even took myself out for dinner and started doing the things for myself that my husband wasn't doing for me.

We were living like roommates for the last two years, but I was the only one wanting him, wanting him to love me, see me, pay attention to me, have sex with me, and be faithful. Apparently, he wasn't interested in me, and so now I have become interested in me.

For now, we are still roommates, but I sense there is a change coming because I realize that I deserve so much more. I realize that God my Father loves me and wants the best for me and my current situation is not my best. I want to be loved, appreciated, dated, married, and sexed. This is definitely not it!

Pick Your Battles

J am so sick and tired of people telling me to pick my battles. Talk to the marriage counselor, and she tells me to pick my battles. Talk to the pastor, and he tells me to pick my battles. How do you pick your battles? Which battles are okay, and which are not okay? What do we do with the ones I shouldn't pick? Isn't that his way of saying he doesn't care?

Let's see. He has cheated the entirety of our marriage. Is that a battle I shouldn't pick? He carelessly spends our money, and then we don't have enough to pay our bills. How about that battle? Should I pick that one?

He likes to leave his clothes on the floor, leaves his poop in the toilet, doesn't lock the doors, house, or car. He tells me that I should go and check after him if I want to make sure the door is locked. So, he comes home late from work or hanging out with his boys, and I need to get up and check to see if he has locked the door?

Are any of those battles I should pick? He goes to pick up the kids, and instead of him coming straight home, he takes them to eat or to his family's house, without picking up the phone and communicating what he is doing. Should I pick that battle?

He stays out late at nights. Sometimes doesn't come home until 1:00 a.m. and doesn't communicate. Should I pick that battle? He says he is a grown man and he doesn't have to tell me anything, and he can come and go as he pleases.

He went riding without his helmet or license and had an accident, and his insurance skyrocketed. The little money I was saving for a rainy day, he used to buy himself a new bike. Should I pick that battle?

I have an idea, how about I start doing some of the crap that he does, and act like an irresponsible child, and see how he feels? Do you think he would want to pick that battle with me?

My coworker has been after me for years. He is sexy, "fine as divine wine," tall, dark, and handsome, and he smells like a man! Perhaps I should go out on a date with him and give him a taste of the cookies. Do you think that's a battle he would want to pick?

How about when he took the kids over to some woman's house and left them in the car for God knows how long and someone called the cops? Should I pick that battle?

The bottom line is, if there is something that's making me uncomfortable, or unhappy, what is wrong with discussing that with my husband? And what is wrong with him working on it? Men go to battle, shoot guns, and sleep in the fields for nights. But I need to pick my battles? What is he? A toddler?

Honestly, I'm tired, and the last battle I am currently picking is the one where the judge says: DIVORCED! How about that battle?

I Just Don't Want to Be Bothered

I didn't remarry because, after my short marriage to a child that was stuck in a man's body, I decided that I just didn't want to be bothered at all with the burden and responsibility of children in grownup bodies. I just don't have the patience to deal with people. I like things a certain way, and I want my life, money, and house a certain way.

I don't want to be bothered with a man leaving the toilet seat up or worse, poop and pee in or on it. I don't want to be bothered with him leaving his clothes on the floor, or hair in the sink when he shaves, or the ring around the tub.

I don't want to be bothered with a man's freeloading family, who thinks just because I have a few dollars I should take care of them, or have them move in my house and destroy my stuff.

I don't want to be bothered with whatever the reason is why he doesn't have enough money to pay his portion of the bills. Because, honestly, I believe a husband is to provide for his wife and family. I don't want to be bothered with him feeling less than a man, or hurting his little ego because I make twice or thrice of what he makes.

I don't want to be bothered with a broken man who is looking for a handout or a hand up. I don't want to be bothered with a man telling me I shouldn't walk into a dealership and pay cash for a car because that's what I want and then I must stroke his ego because he can't.

I'm now in my 40s, and I hear a lot of men in their 50s are starting to have issues in the bedroom. I don't want to be bothered with a ding-a-ling that doesn't work and him not wanting to fix it. I don't want to be bothered with a man who doesn't work out or take care of himself and be healthy.

I don't want to be bothered with a man in my space. Sometimes I just want to sit and enjoy the sunshine or watch the cars drive by. I don't want to be bothered with making him something to eat, or wash his dirty underwear, or dropping clothes off at the cleaners. I just don't want to be bothered.

And that's precisely what happened in my marriage. He got on my nerves so bad that I couldn't stand him. I started to hate everything about him. I just didn't want to be bothered with taking care of him. My momma said it's because I didn't love him. I can honestly say that I loved him. However, I think so much happened in our marriage that I ended up despising him.

When I come home, I just want to sit and read a book or watch a movie. I didn't want to be bothered. In the end, I left him. I got up one day, packed a suitcase, checked into a hotel, and in a month found this beautiful condo that I paid cash for. And yes, it was my own money.

I just didn't want to be, and I still don't want to be, bothered with taking care of a man.

Now, I do believe that if I meet someone that has it together, his faith, finances, health, and wealth, and he is behaving like a man, then perhaps I will see. But until then, I can't be bothered with these men who are trying to get it together and trying to make it.

I Don't Need You to Fix It

*L*ord, my marriage is over! I'm not praying about it; I'm not asking you to fix it! I don't want you to work it out! I shouldn't have married him; I knew it when we were dating, being engaged, and when I married him. I was just hoping it would work, and it hasn't worked out.

I feel as if I have done everything in my power to make it work and did my part. I refuse to waste any more time, and I refuse to keep my children around this mess.

It's over and done! I am ready to move on! All I need is for you to show me the way out! Eighteen wasted years, wasted time, and putting my dreams on the backburner to save my marriage. Now it's over, and it's time for me to live!

JANICE HYLTON-THOMPSON

I Don't Love You Anymore

*W*ould you believe that after I held our household down, worked two jobs and put my husband through medical school, he says to me that he has outgrown me and didn't love me anymore? I was horrified and petrified! I couldn't believe it! We were college sweethearts, and I got a job right out of college because God showed me favor with the Principal that I trained with. He was a year behind me in school. He graduated the following May, and we got married that August.

He decided he wanted to go to medical school, and I was alright with that. Now after teaching and tutoring on the weekends and evenings, taking care of our household, buying us a beautiful home, God finally blessed us with two beautiful children, and now he is Dr. John Doe and has outgrown me?

I thought about going to counseling, but then I wondered why I should run to see a counselor to convince my husband to love me, want me, and to grow with me? I don't want to stay in or work on a marriage with a man who doesn't love me, who doesn't want our marriage or family! I don't want a man who cannot see the sacrifices I made for him, us, and our family!

So, you know what I did? I quickly quit my job and registered to take my Masters in Education. Now it was time for him to take care of our children and me. He could outgrow me as much as he wanted, just pay me my alimony. In court, he told the judge that I had quit my job! The judge put his glasses down on his nose and looked at him and asked who had taken care of him when he was in school. I almost burst out laughing!

My alimony and child support are more than what I was getting from work and tutoring together. So why should I work? I will gladly go to school, work on my masters and my Ph.D., tutor kids for free, and enjoy my alimony. Plus, if I don't remarry I will get half his pension and social security, and he must pay all of my health insurance. Why should I work? I have the last laugh, honey! He has outgrown me, but his money hasn't. #WINNING

It's Too Late

*I*f I had to tell you all that my husband did, it would take a year. It's as if he hated me and he did everything in his power to hurt me. It's not worth repeating, but through it all, I stayed and hoped and waited for him to change his ways and get it right, and become the husband I needed — the man he said he would be.

He finally came around and started to do right and be right. He wasn't hanging out all night anymore; he had begun to help around the house with the kids, laundry, cleaning, and stuff. I don't know if it was the cancer scare or because he was getting older, but he had calmed down a lot.

But, you know what I did? I left. Yes, I sure did leave! I realized that I was no longer in love with him. He was finally doing everything right, but it was too late. Perhaps I didn't understand that I didn't love him anymore because I was so busy trying to hold on to him. Guess he should have loved me when I loved him! He was doing everything too late. I suppose I got tired and didn't realize it. I was trying to hold it together for the children so that their lives were not interrupted by his ungodly ways and the things he did.

I think that sometimes we are too busy fussing, fighting, and carrying on that we don't take time to reflect on how we feel. We are so focused on feeling hurt and angry that we don't realize we don't love the person anymore. The negative emotions keep us from cultivating the right feelings.

I have realized that love is so strong, and yet it's so fragile.

Settling

When I was single and waiting for my husband to find me, I had my list. He had to be a Christian, have a good job, no baby-mama dramas, and educated, tall, dark, handsome, great personality, humble, love the outdoors, etc.

I wasn't meeting anyone, so I decided to throw my list out and settle for him being a Christian and having a job. Wrong decision! Because now, instead of me just enjoying my marriage and the man I'm married to, I'm looking for a way out.

He is arrogant, psychotic and full of himself. He behaves as if he is "the man," but I realize he is just a scared little boy stuck in a man's body!

I knew it was time to go when I was trying to find ways to hurt him. I wanted him to hurt the way he hurt me. I wanted him to cry for many nights the same way I was up crying. I sat a whole afternoon thinking how I could hurt him.

This is the price I had to pay for settling, and compromising on what I wanted in a man. Nevertheless, "Vengeance is mine," says the Lord!

Me, Myself, and I

I have decided that it's best that I stay by myself. Married in my mid-20s and divorced in my early 30s. Presently, I am in my late thirties, and I have not met a suitable man. There's no one out there! They all have something wrong with them: no job, in debt, living with their mothers, baby mama's drama, looking for someone to take care of them, can't provide for a family, don't have a pot to pee in or a window to throw it through! But everyone gets upset with me when I say I don't want to date or marry anyone that doesn't have anything and is not established. I would never marry down or settle.

How is it that a man in his mid to late 40s still doesn't have it together, and is instead looking for someone to take care of him? I don't understand it. I don't understand how men in their thirties and forties are looking for a handout and a woman to build them. When are they going to get it together? I am not trying to take care of a grown man!

I have worked very hard to take care of myself and to provide a comfortable life for my kids and me. I have sought ways to better myself and work on myself so that I can be a better woman and a great wife. I have a great job that has afforded me the ability to purchase a home, to travel, and to live a comfortable life. I am saving towards my retirement, debt-free and have a very nice emergency fund if God forbid, something happens to me, and I am not able to work.

Additionally, I have other streams of income coming in. Therefore, when I meet a man who says he is trying to get it together and he is forty-five, I am puzzled. These are the same men who tell women that they can put their two nickels together and make a dime. They tell women that you can get with me or be lonely. Or you have money, nice car, and a home, but you go home to an empty house with no one to hold you at nights.

Surprisingly, women who are desperate, fall for that crap! Women move these men who are looking for someone to build them up and believe in them, into their homes and lives, and then turn around and be frustrated

151

and fight day and night because they are not working, can't keep a job or won't get a job. I am not about to move a man in my house and life who I need to take care of and provide for.

Not! My Daddy was a hardworking man, and I want a man just like my Daddy. Not a lazy bum that is looking for a hand-out! How is a man who is forty years old, have no credit or is drowning in debt? What am I supposed to do with that? "Work with him and help him to become the man you need him to be" they will tell you. Question: "Who built me up? Who worked with me?

Does that make any sense? I need to get with a man, any man just to say I have a man? He can't do anything for me? He can't provide, can't feed or clothe me! But I need to move him in my big beautiful house with my kids so that I can take care of him? So he can spend my money, eat my food, poop in my toilet and leave my toilet seat up so that I can say I have a man and so that he can hold me? Because I go home to a house without a man and a cold bed? That's the craziest thing I have heard my whole life!!!

This foolish advice that we have gotten from old church mothers has messed up a lot of young women. But not me sweety!!! I am sticking to my guns. If a man is not able to provide and protect me, I have no need for him. I will go and adopt a bunch of kids and love and provide for them because they are children but not a grown man who is looking for a handout and a hand up.

And please don't get me started on these criminals!! I don't do criminals!!!

Switch

For almost two years my husband has been sleeping on the couch, which makes no sense because we have a guest room. So now, after two years of sleeping downstairs on the sofa, he wants to crawl back into my bed?

Now I'm sleeping on the sofa. I won't sleep in the guest room because I don't want him coming in there trying to get in the bed with me.

The marriage is over! Our daughter is away at college, and I've been saving up my money. I have already met with the lawyer, paid half of the money, and I just need to look for a place. I must move because it's his parents' house that they willed him, so I'm not trying to get the house.

For years I begged him to go to counseling and work on our marriage, but he refused. And now he wants to crawl back in my bed, and I need to welcome him with open arms? Sorry, when he wouldn't try to save our marriage, I gave up on him and our marriage a long time ago.

Pretend Play

Have you ever played 'pretend'? Yep, that's my marriage! He likes to pretend that everything is okay when we all know that everything is not good. He doesn't want to talk about our finances, communication issues, sex problems, etc.

He doesn't want to go to counseling or try to resolve any of our issues. He just intends to pretend that everything is okay. We have nothing! No sex, money, communication, friendship, nothing! We don't go to church anymore because we fight like cats and dogs.

So, you know what I decided to do? After five years of marriage and all this foolishness? I've decided to pretend to play with him! All the way to my lawyer's office! Let him act when he is served and when we stand before the judge.

JANICE HYLTON-THOMPSON

I Ain't Going Nowhere

*Y*eah, I know my husband is cheating, has been cheating, and probably won't stop cheating, because, as he said, "I like variety." I worked hard and held him down while he was pursuing his basketball career.

He didn't make the cut, but he went into sports medicine, and the money has been coming in. And now that we got a little something, and I don't have to work as hard. I'm not about to up and leave him cause he's sleeping around!

Yeah, yeah, I know. Some will think I'm foolish, and sometimes I think I am, but the way I look at it is that I'm getting my money's worth. When he didn't have any clothes, I clothed him. When he didn't have anywhere to live and food to eat, I sheltered and fed him.

And now it's time for me to reap my investment. That's just the way I look at it to have a little peace and not to worry and stress about what he's doing out there. All I did was to buy some condoms and tell him that I was not on the pill anymore, so he needed to use them.

I wouldn't tell another wife to leave her cheating husband. Each woman must make that decision for herself. If she can live with knowing that her man is sleeping around, then that's on her.

How Long Am I To Wait?

I was with my husband for 18 years but married for ten years. At our six-year mark, he decided that he was tired of being a husband and family man and needed a break. I can't tell you how devastated I was and the fear I had for my children.

Nevertheless, God gave me the strength to do it all by myself. I waited for him to get himself together. He was sleeping around, and I was the faithful wife! He would come and go as he pleased, and I would keep it together for the kids and me.

Then one day as I walked past my mirror, I had to stop and take a second look at the woman that was looking back at me. I didn't recognize myself. I had bags under my eyes; they were black from crying, I had gained weight, and I had no joy, peace, or happiness. I realized that I wasn't sleeping well because I was worried about my husband. I was concerned about what people were going to say. I was concerned about what the church was going to say.

In a moment, in the twinkling of an eye, courage, and strength came over me. I packed myself and children up, moved out of our home, and moved into a hotel. It was the summer. The kids were off from school, and I had taken about a month off to do me. I realized that I was worth more than what I had settled for.

When I took my vows, I was serious. I meant every word. Unfortunately, my husband didn't take his vows seriously. How long was I supposed to wait for a grown man to get himself together? Honestly, I don't care because I refuse to wait and see. He does not have the privilege to waste my life and my time.

I realized that I had to do what was best for my children and me. I had withered up and died while waiting for him. I wait no longer!

JANICE HYLTON-THOMPSON

Can't You Just Try?

*O*n my Momma's birthday, while getting ready for her party, I asked my husband if he couldn't just make try to save our marriage. You know what he said? "No, I can't try!"

I asked what he had said.

"I said I couldn't try!" He said.

I was disappointed and disgusted all at the same time, and I broke down crying! So, what do I do with a husband who doesn't want to seek to save our marriage? He doesn't want to go to counseling. We have been sleeping in separate rooms for four years and let's not even talk about sex. What do I do?

Should I live in a house with a husband who doesn't want to try to save our marriage and allow my life to pass me by? Should I stay married to say I was married for 20 years? What do I do about my husband who doesn't want me?

It's as if we are two strangers living in the same house. If I don't say "hi" he doesn't say "hey." What is this? This, is not what I prayed for, wanted, or waited for all my life.

I don't know what has happened to us. Somewhere between the kids and us growing up, we grew apart. I still do love him and want us to try and work on the marriage. But he is just not interested.

Stay at Any Cost Possible?

*T*hose old Church Mothers always told us, young ladies, to stick through our marriage at any cost. If he cheated, they said to work it out. If he cheated again, they told us to forgive him and work it out.

They told us to drag him down to the church and let Pastor talk to him if he wasn't acting right. And if he refused to come and talk to Pastor, then invite Pastor over for Sunday dinner so he could talk to him and set him straight.

I believed it because I wanted to be married and have lots of babies. And even when my husband started to act up and behave less than the man God has called him to be, I stayed and prayed. Prayed that God would change his heart and mind and that he would love his children and me enough to be a faithful husband and father.

But, now I am rethinking this "stay at any cost" advice. Stay? At any cost possible? What if the price is my mind, sanity, abuse, depression? What if the cost is an STD? Some STDs can be treated, but what if it is AIDS? What if that cost is my life?

Let me guess what the Church will say: "Stay and trust God that he doesn't get an STD and bring it home to you." Pray that he doesn't kill you? Or separate for a while until he gets himself together and then go back to him?

JANICE HYLTON-THOMPSON

The Fear of Nothing Out There

*W*ent to see the marriage counselor today and I think it's funny how he likes to press the issue to me of there being nothing better out there.

My reply was, "Well, I have nothing here! But leaving him gives me a chance to meet someone possibly."

Out there, there are opportunities, peace, happiness, comfort, safety. Laying in my bed and not having to worry about who my husband is sleeping with. Not worrying about the police knocking on my door because he was driving drunk and there was an accident.

Out there, there is a chance to reinvent me and become a better woman, not a bitter, angry, resentful, and frustrated woman.

Out there, the horizon is the limit. So yeah, I can stay because of fear of what's out there. But Christopher Columbus would have never discovered that Indians lived in America if he hadn't gone out there!

The brave British men and women who wanted religious freedom would have never come to America if they were afraid and hadn't gone out there.

Trust me, out there; it is better than what is in here, even if I must stay by myself for the rest of my life. At least, I will have some peace!

That is a win for me!

Cooking Again

I can't tell you exactly when it happened, but I stopped cooking! I didn't necessarily love to cook, but I liked trying new dishes and would bake here and there. In college, I had a little attic apartment. It was only two small bedrooms, but all my friends, about six of us, would pile up in there and cook and do each other's hair and study. I moved to NY after college, and there was no need to cook as much.

I got married, and *he* loved cooking. We would take turns cooking, and then we got busy and started ordering more and eating out. He was always late coming home, and apparently, he was eating somewhere else, because when I did cook, he wouldn't eat. So, I started working more hours because I knew what the end would be. I would eat at the hospital instead.

Well, it's obvious that my marriage is over and it's only a matter of time before I file for divorce! And guess what? I find myself cooking again! It has brought a smile to my face! I cooked so much food and baked two cakes that I had to invite my nieces and nephews over to eat the food. I'm cooking again!

JANICE HYLTON-THOMPSON

Jealous Not

The nerve of my ex-husband to bring his new girlfriend to my house to meet me! And by girlfriend, I mean 'girl.' My daughter told me she is twenty-five years old. He is fifty-four! Oh, he is such a fool!

Then he called and asked me how I liked her, so I was very nice, and then he asked if I am jealous of her. Jealous? Of what? Living in debt? Ding-a-ling doesn't work, and he only gets four Viagra per month, and that didn't work for him.

I have been very clear that I don't want the children around different women. Only introduce the children to *the one* woman you will have a committed relationship with. But then again, he was married to me and couldn't be committed, and we have children, a house, investments, etc., so how can he commit to one woman now that he is single? Sickening!

Then he called back and asked if he can come over. "HECK, NO!"

Potential Disappointments

Wedding Cake

*T*hree years I kept our wedding cake hoping for us to enjoy it on a beautiful day. In our first year, there was so much turmoil with his cheating and lying.

In our second year, when I was pregnant, he was meeting up in expensive hotels with women he'd met and given his number to. In our third year, the cheating got worse.

One day I was cleaning out the freezer and all the way in the back, I saw our wedding cake. You know the one you're supposed to keep and eat at your first-year anniversary?

Well, I figured we didn't eat it in year one, two, three, and this is year four, so why keep it? I threw it in the garbage and left it on top so that he could see it!

Never Twice

*M*y grandmother told me never to let a man tell you that he doesn't want you twice. Well, I didn't exactly take her advice because five years later, here I am begging my husband to love me, want me, talk to me, spend time with me, take me out and sex me.

She also said, "Baby there is nothing you can do to make a boy take on a man's responsibility. Men will be men, and boys will be boys, and continue to be boys until they decide they are ready to grow up and be men."

Well, twelve years later my little husband is still a kid. When I met my husband, I thought he was such a wonderful man. After a few months of dating, I remember asking why he wasn't married. He said because he wasn't ready and when a man isn't prepared to be married, there is nothing a woman can do to make him ready! Guess he wasn't ready for me either.

Covering Him

My husband was supposed to be my covering, but apparently, I was the one covering him. We were sitting in the counselor's office, and he was asking him questions. I kept answering for him and making excuses for him.

The counselor turned to me and asked why I continued to make excuses for him. He scolded me that my husband acts the way he does because I keep making excuses for him. He doesn't help around the house because he is tired. He doesn't pick up the phone and communicate because he is busy. Everything I was complaining to the counselor about, I was making excuses for him.

Instead of him covering and protecting me, I was the one doing the covering and the protecting because I had allowed him not to take responsibility for his actions.

And he was comfortable with me making excuses for him and covering him. We were college sweethearts, and I grew up and matured, but he was still that 19-year-old boy I had met in college.

Thirteen years later, and he was still that teenager for whom, even though we are the same age, I was going to his professors to beg them not to fail him. I guess I had just taken over where his mother left off.

Angry Black Woman

*C*an you believe he called me an "angry black woman" and said that he was going to leave me for a white woman? I asked him when exactly did I get angry? Was it when he didn't have two nickels to rub together, but I saw the potential in him and gave him a chance. Or, was it when his baby's momma ran off, and I took all three of his kids in and took care of them like my very own?

Or, did I get angry when he didn't work for two years, and I held the family down? We didn't miss a beat because I took up more hours at the hospital so that we could eat, have shelter, and put clothes on our backs. Perhaps it was when he refused to grow up and be a man and stop acting like a little boy, slinging his ding-a-ling in and out of every hole?

He's right! I am angry! Not only am I angry but I am hurt, disappointed, discouraged, and in disbelief that he is not protecting me, us, our children, our family, but has left us destitute. Has anyone taken the time to find out why black women are so 'angry'?

We are angry because our men, who are to be our protectors, are not protecting us. They are not making themselves equipped to provide for us. We take up these men because we see a glimmer of potential in them and they need a little building up and someone to believe in them.

We give them a chance because they cry that black women get our education and a few dollars and then the blue-collar black man isn't good enough anymore. So, why is it that when we give them a chance, they screw our lives up? I am disappointed because I saw potential in him and nothing has happened. Disappointed because I gave him a chance and he messed up my life and my finances!

He is supposed to be our provider, but can't even keep a job. He is expected to be the prophet for our family, but he won't even go to church and submit to God.

But he wants to call me and many other hurt and disappointed sistas angry? Maybe our men need to take the time to find out why we are so angry? What have you done to cause us to be angry?

I'm Sorry for Trying to Change You

*W*hen I was packing to move out of our home because of a court order to sell it and split the profits, I found a journal that had a list of what I had wanted in a husband. It was written when I was 20 years old and was praying for my husband. It brought tears to my eyes because I had married a man who didn't meet many of the things I had prayed for. I guess I got weary and gave up on God and settled for him.

After reading over my list, I called him and apologized, because I should not have married him but walk away instead. He wasn't what I had prayed for or wanted, but I had married him, hoping that he would change his ways and become the husband I had prayed for and desired.

I had wanted him to be a godly and faithful husband, but at every chance he got, he was sleeping around. I knew he was cheating while we were dating and engaged. I had wanted him to call or text me throughout the day, but he could go a whole day without texting or calling. I had wanted him to call me the minute his flight landed whenever he was traveling, but he would land, take a car to his hotel, get into bed, and not even call to say, "Honey, I got here safely." And his excuse would be "I forgot" or "I was sleepy."

I had wanted a godly husband who reads his Bible and prays, but he couldn't even find Genesis or bless our food while we had been dating. I had wanted a man who loved children and wanted to be a father, but I had to fight with him to give me children, and then he didn't want to be bothered with them. He was always too tired or busy or sleepy.

I had wanted someone such that we could grow together and have things in common, but the truth is that we never became one. He had no interest in the things I liked, and he didn't want me to participate in the activities he liked. Merely asking him to explain something about sports would turn into a big fight.

The truth is, I knew many of these things when we were dating and engaged, but I went ahead and married him anyway, knowing that he wasn't what I prayed for or wanted. I was hoping that he would change for me. It's all my fault!

My Dream Man

I was wrong for marrying this man! I married a couch potato and wanted him to become a gym rat. At least, that's what he said when we started to date — "I am very athletic, played volleyball in high school and college." So, when I met my husband, I wasn't interested because he looked like a couch potato, but he was a nice guy.

I decided to give him a chance with the understanding that he needed to lose weight and get on an exercise regimen. He agreed and even lost about ten pounds. That was where his exercising ended. We went to a beautiful resort for our honeymoon that had a state of the art gym. Not once did he come to work out with me.

About a year into my marriage of encouraging him to go with me to the gym and eat the healthier meals that I prepared, I realized that I didn't fall in love with the man that was standing in front of me, but I fell in love with his potential. Who he said he would be. I didn't fall in love with the 50-year-old man with a 50-year-old body that has never seen the inside of a gym. I fell in love and married the 50-year-old that was going to go to the gym and become like The Rock.

I didn't fall in love with the man who had no stamina and couldn't hold his own in the bedroom. I fell in love with the man who was going to do what he needed to do to have the stamina of a man half his age so he could put my back out! Guess I should have married that younger man!

At the same time, I am 43 years old, and I don't have the body of a regular almost-50-year-old because I exercise. People say it doesn't matter, what a person's body is like, but that is not true. Not only are men visual, but women are too. We get turned on by what we see also. Nothing is dropping or hanging; everything is standing at attention.

And no, it's not only physical but everything matters. Faith, personality, finances, health, physical fitness, sense of humor, and so on. When we pledge to share our lives with someone, we need to do everything we can to make us our very best. Not working out while you are steadily gaining weight is not being our very best for ourselves and our mates.

Help Wanted!

*S*ometimes, I'm not sure if I married a grown man or a child that needs to be trained. I can't compare him to my teenage son who is away at college because he is more of a man than my husband is.

Please help me with this! How does a grown man come in the house by unlocking two locks but locks only one back? His excuse — "I'm rushing to get the alarm." Well, the alarm has 30 seconds on it, and it only takes a second to lock the second lock!

Put the code in the alarm to unlock it and walk away without locking it. His excuse — "I forgot." So, all you need to do is press 1, 2, 3, 4, lock. No, he presses 1, 2, 3, 4 and walks away!

Maybe you can answer this one for me? How does a grown man leave loads of poop in the toilet and not make sure it's flushed? Not once, twice, or three times, but all the time! His excuse — "I was rushing" or "I forgot!" And leave the toilet seat up all the time. His excuse — "I forgot." One day I went off and guess what he said? — "I can't believe you are getting upset about a lil bit of crap!" Unbelievable!

How about this one? Leaves his clothes on the floor instead of putting it in the hamper that is right there. You take your clothes off, and you put it in the basket! His excuse — "Why don't you do it since you have a problem with it?"

Here's another one! Goes to hang out with the boys and doesn't come home till 2-3 a.m. and does not communicate. His excuse — "Baby, I lost track of time!" Gets caught cheating and guess what he said? — "Baby, that was a mistake. You know I love you!"

Now, I have done a great job by raising my son as a single mom, and then married this "man" who I thought could be a father figure for my son, and this is your example? I don't think so! Goodbye!

Threesome

I'm having a threesome or a love triangle marriage. It's me, my husband, and his momma! I knew he was a momma's boy, and you know the saying, "If he loves his momma, he'll love you." Well, I think he loves her more than he loves me. And another thing is, she doesn't even like me. She liked his ex, but she broke up with him and married someone else. I think he might have been on the rebound when we started dating. I knew his momma didn't like me, but I didn't believe it would be this bad. The truth is, I can't stand her either.

If I say A and she says B, he does B. He spends more time at her house than he does over here. He eats over there more than he does over here. Everything I cook, he always comments that it doesn't taste like his momma's cooking.

The straw that broke the camel's back was when I was in the hospital having our son, and his mother refused to come and be with us there. Then he left me in the hospital during labor to take her to her to Bingo! Yes, you heard me right! He left me in the hospital to take his mother to her Bingo game. I was flabbergasted. Thank God, my mom walked in just as he was leaving. I was in the hospital for almost a week because I had a C-section and she didn't even come to see us.

But on the way home from the hospital, he stopped by her condo, so she could see the baby and he begged me to get out of the car. I refused! Then, he asks me what Jesus would do? I didn't even look at him.

Then when he came back out with the baby, guess what he said? "Momma said he doesn't look like our breed of the family!" I cursed him and his momma out and told him to take me to my momma's house!

Finances/Money

$1.20

$\mathcal{I}$ divorced my husband for $1.20! Well, at least that's what he's running around telling people and the counselor. For the entirety of our marriage, he made bad financial decisions! He spends money as if we go into the backyard and pick if it off trees; as if he doesn't know the value of a dollar.

If I knew he was this financially incompetent, I would not have married him. He was so bad that I signed us up for a financial workshop for two months just so that he can understand how important money is. How we can't spend every penny, live paycheck to paycheck, and how we need to save.

I felt like I am married to a child I am trying to teach the value of money. And then when it's time to pay the bills, he comes and asks me how we are going to pay this bill and that bill.

The last incident was when I wrote out exactly what I wanted him to buy and that it was $1.20 difference. When he came home, of course, he didn't get the item that I had written down on the paper. I went off. I felt my blood pressure rising because we had just had our lights cut off because he hadn't paid the bill.

I remember running, screaming and going into the bathroom and closing the door until I calmed down. Right there and then, I decided that I could not stay in that marriage. It was too stressful for me.

In all my years of living, even when my mom was struggling to make ends meet, we never had our lights off. We always had roof, food, lights, water, and clothes if the money was there.

Even the counselor thought I was too dramatic about the $1.20. But I explained that my husband has not made one good financial decision our whole marriage and that I just can't live with him anymore. If I stay with this man, I will end up in the poor house, no roof over my head or food on my table.

$60K Mistake

*H*e would always ask me to allow him to make a mistake. So, would the Pastor and marriage counselor. So, I shut up and let him make a mistake, and over the last three years, and am still counting. To date, his mistakes have cost us over $60K, and he has no plans of stopping. When I spoke to him along with the counselor who told me to allow him to make a mistake, he said that he had no plans of changing or fixing the issue.

It seems that he has no intention of listening to me and doesn't care about me and our family's well-being. For the last three years, we have been living paycheck to paycheck, something I didn't have to do as a single woman. However, now pressured to do as a married woman, I think it's time for me to make a decision and leave.

I have worked too hard as a single woman to provide a comfortable life for myself, only to get married and struggle. When I was single, I wasn't struggling. My income was more than enough for me. And now, I am married, and he has his very own income, but because of this leak that he refuses to plug, he has caused me to be in debt and struggling. I just can't! Three years is more than enough time for this!

Well, half of that money is mine, and I don't want to waste any more of it, plus I need to pay my lawyer almost $500 per hour to sort out all this mess.

THE NAKED WIFE

$250,000.00

The sheriff with two other people in suits walked up in my garden at the back of the house. I went to meet them, wondering what was going on. Had something happened to one of my boys? No!

They had come to arrest me because my husband had taken out a $250,000.00 loan and signed my name to pay it back if he wasn't able to. I almost fainted and was in disbelief as they handed me the paper with his signature and my name to pay it back. The payments were already nine months behind because six months ago my husband had died of a heart attack.

He had also put up the house as collateral which broke my heart because that was all we had. I was planning to sell the house to put the boys through college. I cannot begin to tell you how heartbroken I was. I stood there in my backyard and cried as if my mother had died! This man had gambled away everything we had, and now the house was gone too? No wonder that bastard died of a heart attack!

He was a police officer, but he was so careless and irresponsible with money. When he got paid, he would cash his check and drink and gamble it all off and would come home empty-handed. Even after many fights and quarrels, he continued to do the same thing repeatedly.

Eventually, the light came on, and I decided that every payday I would go to the police station and take the check from him, cash it, give him some, and use the rest for the family. I hated having to do that, but unfortunately, that is the idiot I married.

And for 25 years, that was what I had to do, or else we wouldn't have been able to survive. It was so embarrassing that I had to do that. It was as if he was a child and I needed to be his mother. It was discouraging and draining, but for the sake of my boys, I decided to stay with the old drunk. I tried to save everything and everyone and then ended up losing it all.

JANICE HYLTON-THOMPSON

A Special Man

*I*t takes a special kind of man that will be comfortable with his wife making more money than he does. I am very traditional. I believe a man is to provide for his family. Unfortunately, I didn't meet anyone who made what I made, or close to it. And then, like my daddy said, maybe I should broaden my horizon.

So, I met this sweet Brother at one of our churches. It took me time to get it out of my head that he didn't make much, and by 'much' I mean in comparison to me.

We got married, and he wanted me to sell my house so that we could get one together. I agreed and put my house on the market. We got a lovely home a few cities over from where my house was. But I could tell how uncomfortable he was with my income. He wanted to put down 3-5% while I wanted us to put down more than 20% to make a dent in the loan. (I hate debt.)

Anyways, I tried very hard to make him comfortable. We had a joint account where both of our pays went in, and we paid the bills from that account. Whenever we went out, I allowed him to pay and never pulled my wallet out.

When things needed to be fixed around the house, he fixed them, and I would never bring money up because he would always make smart remarks about me buying stuff. I would buy what I wanted or needed. He wanted me to ask him for permission. Sorry, I'm not going to ask if I can buy myself a new pocketbook! That's just not going to happen!!

Then, it seemed as if we had fights daily about money, which made no sense because we had more than enough for everything. So, why were we always fighting about money?

White Boy Love

*I*t is time for black women to stop being faithful to black men because they are not faithful to us! Honestly, I was not open to marrying a white man. I attended one of our most prestigious Universities. And of course, there were maybe two black men on the whole campus. It was so depressing because I had always said I wanted an educated black man.

Well, I graduated, started working as a teacher, and was still not meeting a decent black man that I would even have coffee with. Then, my friend from college, Melanie, had a birthday party and here came my knight in shining armor. I kid you not; I fell head over heels in love with that white boy instantly! It was as if God had opened my eyes and boom! We dated and were married in a year. We had a beautiful little wedding on sunny spring day.

He is a social worker, and five years into our marriage, I became the principal making almost thrice what he made. Can I tell you that after twelve years of marriage, and three babies later, we have never had one fight about money? Not one! We live a modest life in a modest home and drive modest vehicles. We live on his income, and save mine for the retirement, vacations, and children's college funds. We pay our tithes and offerings, and we give when there's a need. We lack nothing, and my husband has never had an issue with me making more money than he does. It doesn't even come up.

But some of my friends who make way less than me are married to men who make pennies, and they always have fights about money! I have a friend who makes $50K, and her husband makes $35K, but he is always arguing with her about what she buys and how she thinks she is better because she makes more. I just don't understand the insecurity of some men who are not comfortable with their wives making more money than they do.

I don't have to ask my husband's permission to buy anything. We both have a $500 spending limit, and if we are spending more than that, just an

"FYI" is needed. But, to fight about buying a pair of shoes for $50? That has never happened with us.

I tell my single girlfriends all the time to leave Faquan and get them a Justin! Not my Justin though! LOL!!

Men and Money

On a good year, I gross anywhere from $375K to $450K. Gurl, it is very, very hard to meet a black man who makes $100K, much less $500K. I had the most difficult time dating because eventually, the money talk would come up, usually by the guys when they wanted to get serious. I was even engaged and was so afraid of losing him that I didn't tell the whole truth about how much I made. When he finally came out and asked, and I told him, he almost had a heart attack.

Then we started having issues and then we broke up because he was not comfortable being with a woman who made more.

But time went by, and I was not getting married or having children. Then I was blessed to be able to do some traveling and could move around more freely. By the time I hit 40, I had already given up on the whole husband-and-babies thing. Even though women are having babies well into their 40s and even 50s, that was not going to be me!

Anyways, the Lord smiled on me, and I met a very nice African-American man, a divorced dad of two. This was great because I had always wanted children but just never had any. We dated, courted, and we both sat down with our lawyers and drew up some papers and, yes, we signed a prenup. He grossed about $250K per year. We came up with a plan that worked for us.

To date, we have been married eight years, and we have not had any fights or arguments about money. He said he had made many mistakes in his first marriage and he was financially irresponsible. Because of his irresponsibility, it destroyed his marriage. When his wife divorced him, he saw that he needed to work on his behavior with money.

About half of his income goes to his ex-wife for alimony and child support, but we still have more than enough for us. What I realized is that a man has to be secure about who he is for him to be comfortable with his woman making more than he does. When we go out, I don't even bring my wallet with me, because I know he has it covered. When we went shopping for a new car for my birthday, I allowed him to sign on the dotted line.

I just feel so secure with him, because he is secure about who he is. Money is never an issue for us. Based on the stories I have heard about men being upset about their women making more, I have not experienced that with my husband. And after eight years, I have stopped fearing it, and am just resting in being with a secure man.

Prenup

*I*f a woman is in her thirties and older and has a little something, why would you want to get married without a prenup? I have been on my own since I was seventeen when my parents kicked me out because I got pregnant. My aunt, who didn't have any kids, took me in and raised my daughter and I like her own.

Since I had a child and was on public assistance, I was able to get free financial aid, and I went on to become a lawyer. My uncle — my aunt's husband — was a lawyer and had lawyer friends who hired me, and I did pretty well for myself.

I met my guy when I was thirty-six and by the time I was thirty-seven he proposed. We didn't discuss money much because we were both doing financially well. He was a social worker, so there weren't any financial issues.

One day while at lunch, I asked him what he thought about prenups. He said he would not sign one and that it is just saying we don't trust each other, and if we love each other then we don't need one. I stated that I would like for us to sign a prenup because I have worked very hard to build a nest egg for my daughter, and I wanted to make sure that her interests were protected. He mentioned that he was not concerned about that for his daughter.

I asked him about the plans, savings, and investments he had for his daughter, and he said he had none.

I asked him if he knew that according to our State Law, if the marriage didn't work, everything had to be split 50/50, and he asked what was wrong with that. I choked!

I asked him what he had just said. All my investments, retirement accounts, all of the properties I had, everything split 50/50? Did he think that was fair?

He said we didn't have to worry about that because we were not getting a divorce.

So, I asked him if he had life and car insurance. He said yes! I asked why if he had planned on having an accident or dying anytime soon? He said "no."

But what if he had an accident? What if he died soon, would his daughter be taken care of?

Yes!

So, what was the difference between his life and car insurance, and a prenup to make sure that my daughter's interests were protected?

No answer!

I gave him the ring back a few months later. Sorry, I have worked too hard to build a life for my daughter and myself to risk it all. People are quick to say that's planning to have a divorce. Broke and poor folks get divorced every day!

And why wouldn't you want to make me comfortable? How do I know you are not after my money? If you love me and you don't want my money, if you just want me, then sign the prenup. Sorry, I will stay by myself and hold my pillow before I marry a man that doesn't want to sign a prenup. I want more kids, and God has blessed me to afford a lot of them with a live-in nanny. So, I will adopt. There are a lot of kids that need a nice home.

If I meet a man who is well off and he asks me to sign a prenup, I don't mind signing and would in a heartbeat. Because I have my own money, I have worked hard to provide a comfortable life for my daughter and myself.

How well am I financially? Truth? I can retire at forty if I want to. And I just might. I have always wanted to teach law, so I have been thinking of resigning from the law firm, and getting an adjunct position at my alma mater, teach law, and possibly adopt a few kids.

Benz in The Hood

J am used to living a particular lifestyle. My parents paid for my college so; I didn't have any debts. I worked hard to take care of myself and help my family where I can. Got a beautiful 2-bedroom apartment in one of our city's newest developments and I'm just living and enjoying life.

But there were just two things that were missing: husband and baby! I wanted to be married! I have been in Church my whole life and served in the ministry, but just didn't meet anyone. Finally, I met my now-husband. He was married before and is a single dad, and I admired him. He is a faithful brother in the church and a great father overall.

We dated for about a year and finally got married. I was disappointed that he didn't want us to have a big wedding because he said it was a waste of money, but I submitted to his leading and had the cutest little church wedding and reception at our church.

I wanted to go to Jamaica for our honeymoon, and he said that was a waste of money. So, we went somewhere nearby for the weekend. Then he insisted that I give up my beautiful apartment because it was too much money. I rented it because I didn't want the responsibility of owning.

I was petrified because we had initially agreed that we would live there. But no! He wanted me to move back to the inner city where the rent was cheaper. I asked him if he realized that I drove a Benz. He said that I needed to get something cheaper. I told him no because my parents had bought that for me for my fortieth birthday present. That upset him!

Then he said I spent too much money buying red bottomed shoes and I needed to buy cheaper shoes, so he took me to Payless! I almost fainted!! I wear Mac makeup, and he said that cost too much, and that he had seen beautiful makeup at his favorite store for cheap — Family Dollar. I was horrified!!!

He won't allow me to go to the mall alone because he said he didn't want me spending any money! This, is my issue! I was living at a level that was comfortable for me. Why it is that now that I am married, I am living below what was suitable for me?

Like Pastor always said, a man is to complement and enhance a woman's life and vice versa. Why do I feel so oppressed? And when I speak up, then there is a lot of tension between him and me. He wants me to just say "Yes, Sir" to everything he says, and not to have an opinion!

One day he asked me if I was mad because he didn't want us wasting "our" money.

I looked at him and said, "Our money?" I wanted to ask him what he was talking about. I make three times what he makes, so how is it "our" money? How come I can't spend any of 'our' money? But I bit my tongue.

I suggested that we both put a portion of our pay in a joint account for house expenses, and then we both keep some so that we could have spending money. He said there was no need for that.

Yep, think it's time to meet with Pastor and First Lady, because I don't believe that this is what the Bible meant when it says, "Wives, submit to your husbands." "I'm here for now, but this doesn't look promising at all."

I Don't Believe in Prenups

I just don't think that saints should sign prenups. I think that is a sure plan that the marriage will fail, and we should love each other and work out any issues we have. If you have a prenup, then you are just planning for a divorce.

I used to believe that! That was until the judge told me that I must pay my ex three years of alimony! I think I fainted in the courtroom! Alimony? Yes, alimony, and sell our home and split the profits! The home that he couldn't even come up with half of the down-payment for!

So much for marrying a man that makes less than me! Never again will I date, marry, or even talk to a man that makes less than me. It's a waste of my time. I had to pay that scum alimony? I was livid!

And you know, when I was getting married, my daddy told me to sign a prenup, and I had said, "No, church folks shouldn't sign prenups, and we need to trust God!"

Well, I believed God and what did I get? Three years of paying a man alimony because I made four times what he did? We fight all the time about money. For what reason, I don't know. He felt that I was putting away money, but that is something I have always done. Save for a rainy day, retirement, ROTH IRA, and so on. Thank God, the judge didn't make me split that up.

I don't know what we are supposed to do as single women. Many women today are making a whole lot more than our counterparts. Women with big incomes are not meeting men who are in our income bracket. Therefore, it's either take a chance with a man who makes less or stay alone because if it doesn't work out, you will end up having to pay him!

That man was so insecure about my few dollars that I refused to have kids with him. It was too stressful. From the time we got engaged, to the wedding, honeymoon, and the car I bought myself for my 40th birthday that I have been saving toward for five years, to me breathing, it seemed like.

When I came in the house with a new pair of shoes, he behaved as if he wanted to fight me. SMH!!

Two Fools

*I*f I can think of a word to describe my husband and me, it would be 'foolish!' Why? Well, let's see. The fights that we are having now were the same fights we were having when we were dating and engaged. We fought about money when we were engaged too. So, what made me think that it would be different when we got married?

He told me he was in debt and I asked him what he was doing to work on his debts. He said he was doing nothing because he couldn't afford to pay them right then! He was paying his child support, and after that, there was not much left.

Well, that's stupid, I thought! If he wasn't working on his credit and paying his debts while he was single, and it was just him and had more finances available, why would he work on it when we got married?

Isn't the whole reason of preparing for marriage to rid yourself of as much baggage as possible? Why would you wait until marriage to work on your debts? A better question is; why did I marry him knowing that he had all those debts and had done nothing to work on them? Truth? I was foolish! I was hoping he would change. He was paying his child support, so I thought this was a good guy, and he had potential.

But then we got married, and he had all his previous child support and garnishments on his check that the government took when we filed taxes. I often think of the scripture that says two become one. Apparently, two becoming one meant that his debts became my debts too. I cannot live in this financial bondage situation.

A Curse

I do believe that when I married my husband, a curse came on me and my finances. Before I married him, I was doing great financially. I had a beautiful 3-bedroom condo, investments, savings, and so on. You name it; I had it. My parents paid for my college and gave me the down-payment on my condo. They are both accountants and taught my brother and me not to get into debt and to live beneath our means, etc.

While they always taught us to not get into debt, they also taught us to pay what we owed if we did. They always warned us not to marry people who were in debt, and that their debts would become ours. So why did I marry a man drowning in debt? Now that we are married, I am seeing that he didn't tell me the whole truth about his debts.

A year into our marriage, his sister got into trouble, and we had to bail her out. I had almost $30,000.00 saved up, and we used it to bail her out of jail for some insurance fraud mess. It has been three years, and I still have not seen a dime of that money back.

Can I tell you that we are in debt up to our heads? I can't even let my parents know how bad things are! I don't like not having enough, and living from paycheck to paycheck. It makes me sick just talking about it.

We're so broke we can't even pay our tithes and offerings!

Why Did I Get Married?

There has been a lot of tension in our marriage. Honestly, I want out! We went to counseling and Pastor separated us. He asked me, "Why did you get married to John?"

I gave the typical religious response, "Oh he is a man of God, he's a praying man, blah blah blah…"

A few weeks later, as I was having my time with the Lord, the question came up in my mind. "Why did you get married to John?" I had to search my heart and accept that I got married for financial security. That's what my Momma always told me. Marry a man who can take care of you. She didn't say anything about love, communication, affection, similarities, etc. Marry a man who is Christian and who can financially provide.

I think deep down that was always on my conscience and that was what I did. But the problem is, even though he makes a lot of money, he is so financially irresponsible that we are not financially secure. There have been times that I had to use my whole paycheck to pay the mortgage. I am doing worse now financially than when I was single.

And now he is talking about having babies? Who's having babies in this financial catastrophe? Not me! When I have children, I would like to take a whole year to stay home with my baby. Plus, he has gotten us into so much debt that there is no way I would bring a child into this world with him right now.

I have exhausted all my savings. My credit cards are all maxed out trying to make ends meet. I think God is punishing me. In all of my adult life, I have never struggled financially as I am now that I am married.

189

One Thing

*M*arriage and a family was the *one* thing I wanted more than anything else. Other people want to be millionaires, have a big house, but for me? I wanted to have a family. So, the thought of my marriage not working out makes me sick to my stomach. I wanted to throw up and stayed in bed for a whole week. My girlfriends even got a counselor to come to the house to see me.

Just talking about it now makes me nauseated. I have never, in my whole life, seen someone as stubborn as my ex-husband was. I mean it was as if he was rebellious against everything I asked him to do. My breaking point was when he cosigned for his brother to get a truck. After I begged him not to do it because his brother wasn't working, and his unemployment was running out, he went ahead and cosigned anyway and used $3000 out of our emergency fund to pay down on the truck, which I hadn't agreed to. He reasoned that he needed transportation to look for jobs.

We were saving and working on his credit so that we could purchase our first home. He needed me to give $400 out of my child support money that I get for my daughter to help his brother pay his truck and insurance. I gave it to him and asked him to check to see what bills were coming in until we got paid again so I that could put enough money in the joint account to cover the mortgage and the other expenses.

I had to ask him four times. He was leaving to go hang out with his brother, and I asked how much I needed to write a check for, and that I was waiting.

His response was, "You could have come down and seen it on the table!"

I went off! You can come to me and ask me for money to make sure your brother's truck is paid for, but you can't let me know how much we need to make sure our mortgage and expenses are paid?

I need to put more in the joint account, which he oversees, but it was too much for him to tell me how much more I needed to add? I sat at the table for the next three hours just staring into space, and I knew I had to get away from him. Many months, if my daughter's father weren't paying me child support, we would not be able to make ends meet.

His grown-behind brother is driving around in a brand new, fully loaded truck being paid for by me and my husband, while I'm driving around in a broken-down caravan because I am trying to save every penny so that my kids can have a home of their own! What's wrong with that picture?

Why should I stay married to him? He doesn't care about me and my concerns, our financial security, and safety, or our future. I'm busy saving every penny to buy a home for our kids, while he is spending money like a spoiled teenager. Why do bad with a man when I can do bad alone with my children?

Drastic Steps

A year into our marriage, my husband came to me and said that he needed to help his family out for a few months financially. I asked how many months was a few months and he said six months. I told him that as long as it was only six months, it was okay and that it would dent us, but we could recover.

Additionally, I was pregnant and had planned to take a year's maternity leave. I also asked him to keep me posted on the situation and that I didn't want to come and ask him for updates. When three months passed without an update, I asked. He got upset and had a fit. Six months later, there was still no update. So, I called a marriage counselor.

A year later, nothing changed, and I was not able to take the time I would have liked for maternity leave. Two years later, nothing changed, except that there was a lot of tension and fighting in our home. Three years later, the marriage counselor instructed me to ask my husband about the update. He looked at me and said, "All of the counselors we have seen have told you that. That's not going to change."

I felt as if someone had thrown a bucket of ice water on me while I was standing outside in only my underclothes in the middle of winter. To make matters worse, I was going to work every day trying not to miss any days, because we couldn't afford for me to miss even a day of work. Rain, sun, shine, snowstorm, sickness or tiredness, I went to work every day trying to keep us afloat.

A month later, the light came on for me. It was apparent that he had no plans of fixing this issue or finding a resolution for it. Also, that this could go on for another three years. Since he told me that he was not going to change or fix the issue, I decided that I was going to change.

I decided that I was going to stop contributing to keeping us afloat, and the most significant bill, which was the mortgage, would lapse. I had to come up with all the mortgage payment many months because he wasn't able to pay it with whatever he had "left over" after he had made sure his family's expenses were taken care of.

So, I changed! I refused to contribute to any bills and only made sure the water and electricity were paid for, and that there was food for the kids. When the cable went out, he asked me for my bank card, and I said "no." When the car insurance came, and he told me to pay it, I said "no." When the insurance company canceled the insurance, I took the bus to work and dropped the kids off at daycare.

When it was time for the mortgage and I needed to add $1200 for it to be paid, I said "no." He told me to stop the foolishness and write him a check, and I said "no." The day of the mortgage he asked again, and I said "no." 5 p.m., he asked, and I said "no." He said he was going to write a check and that I needed to put the money in the account so that the mortgage could be cleared, but I said "no."

The mortgage check bounced, and the downward spiral began. The bank called, and the letters started to come, and we fought and argued more. And then the letters from the bank began to come more, and he continued to make sure his extended family's bills were paid while our home went into foreclosure.

Time went by, and the house was in foreclosure. Then the sheriff came and put the notice on the door that we had less than a month to vacate. I was already packing the children and my things up along with some furniture while he looked at me as if I was crazy. And then the sheriff came and put the notice on the door that we had so much time to move and then that's when he wanted to talk and find a resolution to his issue.

Nope, too late!! I had applied for a beautiful 3-bedroom garden apartment a few cities over, and that was approved. He wanted to move with us, and I told him "no," that the marriage was over, and I was not going to take the burden with me. The children and I moved out, and we left him there and one day he came home, and the sheriff had locked the door.

Unfortunately, that was the drastic step I had to take, and when all was said and done, we all suffered. My children suffered the most because their routine had changed. We lost our home and daddy was no longer in our household. But, putting my foot down with him was also the best thing I could have done for my children and me because he had no intention of manning up and putting his foot down to his family and demand that they became self-sufficient and stop depending on him hand and foot.

I filed for divorce, and he wanted to settle child support out of court, and I told him "no," that based on what happened, I was not convinced that he would make sure he paid, so I went through the courts. I don't know what is going on with that situation now, and honestly, I don't care. I finally had to tell my dad about what happened after it was all done, and of course, he was upset with me and asked why I hadn't called him.

I didn't let my father know because I knew that he would get on the next plane and bring me a check. But why should he? My husband sat across from my daddy at his dinner table and asked him for my hand in marriage. My dad told him that I was his baby girl and the only girl he had, and for him to take care of me.

To me, when a man asks a woman's father for her hand in marriage, the father is no longer responsible for her, and now her husband has taken on full responsibility for her. So, no, I refused to call my dad for help because of my husband, who was supposed to be my head, covering, and leader and was to make sure he took care of me. Not my father!

And let me share my testimony. My daddy is so great, that he told me not to settle in where we were but to try and find a house. He always believed that children are to be raised in a home of their own, not in apartment buildings. Since I had signed a year's lease, I stayed the year, and after my lease was up, we closed on a beautiful 5-bedroom-4 bath house with a huge backyard. Daddy practically paid for the whole thing. God is so good!!!

I always wanted a man like my dad. He is such a man's man!!

Providers
vs.
Nurturers

Potential?

I'm sorry; I am not a ride-or-die chick! I have struggled to get to where I am today. There is no way on God's green earth that I'm going to work my fingers to the bone to take care of a man who apparently is comfortable with me making the bacon, bringing it home and cooking it and serve it to him before I serve my children.

It has been three years since he lost his job. I think in three years he has been on two job interviews. I brought home fast food applications. He told me he's not doing that. Fine, I suggest he get his college education, he said no. Where I come from, you do what you can do until something better comes along.

I've been carrying all these bills by myself for three years. I mean his income wasn't much from the beginning, but at least I knew the energy bill, and car payments would be made. Now, I'm carrying a mortgage and all, and it pisses me off that every evening when I come home, there is a grown man in my living room playing video games. What thirty-five-year-old man plays video games all day long?

Now, I will admit, when I met him, he didn't have much and wasn't doing much. But he had potential, and you know the older folks always said if you meet a man who has a little potential, then give him a chance. The problem is that twelve years later, I'm still waiting for the potential to manifest itself.

I've had to borrow money from my Daddy trying to make ends meet, and it is frustrating that I have a grown man in the house doing nothing! I sold his truck that I was paying for to help around the house. He got mad and went to his momma's house for a month.

She called me and asked me why I hadn't come to see my husband, and for me to come and get him because he wouldn't leave and was eating all of her food. I told her that she needed to let him stay over there because he was acting like a child and she was his mother. She packed him up and brought him back to my house.

50/50

$\mathscr{W}$ e were college sweethearts and came from the same church organization. We dated on and off through college but went our separate ways after graduation. Seven years later we reconnected and started dating. Two years later we got married, and we made a decent income for our professions. He worked in the insurance field, and I was teaching at a private Christian School.

My husband made $70K, and I made $40K. Before we got married, we agreed that we would pay the bills together from one account. Well, we got married, and he said he realized that he was paying more than me and that since I was on his health and dental insurance, I needed to pay more of the household expenses. I told him yes; because he earned more, it meant more of his income went toward the expenses.

We got into a big fight one day. He said that I needed to start paying 50/50 of everything because it was not fair. If I didn't have my 50%, then I needed to get another job.

What? "We have more than enough to cover our expenses!" I said.

"Well, you better have your 50% next month, or else we need just to end this right now!"

"You want to end our marriage because you are paying more of the expenses?"

"Yep," he said.

Blinds & Training Bra

*A*ll I wanted for Christmas was a training bra for my baby girl and some blinds. My husband was so cheap that cheapness should be declared a disease. He was so cheap that he would only put $5 of gas in the car; enough for me to go to the supermarket and come home. I had to walk 12 blocks to drop the kids off and pick them up from school because he didn't want to waste money. Be it rain, snow, or sun; we had to walk.

He didn't allow me to work, which made no! Why not allow me to work to bring in some extra money? Trying to be a submissive Christian wife, I respected his decision. He was so cheap that we only had one TV and one cable box because he said it was a waste of money. I had to let the kids watch TV after school until he got home because once he was home, he didn't share the TV with us. That is when the kids did their homework. I had to wake the kids up at 5 a.m. on the weekends so they could watch their cartoons until he decided to wake up, and then he hogged the TV all day.

Thank God for my mom and dad. One year, they bought the kids one of those TVs with the VCR and CD player built in, plus about 50 different movies and cartoons. That was the best Christmas gift ever! He was upset and told them not to use up all his electricity.

My breaking point came when my little girl turned 9 and was asking for a cartoon training bra. My little boy wanted a pair of light-up sneakers, and I wanted some blinds for the house for Christmas. He wouldn't give us any money because he said it was a waste and we didn't need all of that.

Six months before, my aunt had died and willed her house and some money to me. She didn't have any children, and she had always treated me as her own, even though her brothers and sisters, my aunts and uncles, had tried to fight it. Once everything was cleared with the lawyer, he brought me a check for $20K. I cried and shouted for joy, and then the kids came, and I told my daughter she could get her bra and my son his light-up sneakers. Meanwhile, he was sitting at the table like he had drunk a bottle of lemon juice.

198

Once the lawyer left, he took the check and said that we needed to deposit it and that we needed to let it stay in the bank for a while to make sure everything was okay.

"Christmas is in 3 weeks!" I yelled.

He told us not to worry, that he would take care of it. The kids and I stayed up all night and talked and planned what we could do and buy.

Days before Christmas, I asked for the money, and he brushed it off. Later that day he came home, and guess what he drove up in? A brand-new truck! Where is the money I need to buy the kids' stuff for Christmas? "Oh, that's foolishness!" He said. I burst out crying, screaming and yelling. The kids came outside, the neighbors came out, and I was fighting him. Thank God, my neighbor grabbed me because I had picked up the shovel to smash the truck. Oh, it was a big thing!

My baby couldn't get a training bra for $9.99, but he used my $20K to buy a new truck? I thank God for my neighbor who suggested that we should go down to the bank, so they can put a stop payment on the truck and get my money back. It was just a big mess! But that day was my breaking point, and I knew I had to get away from that bastard!

I called my parents, and they came and got us. We left everything except what my parents had bought us, and the kids and I moved into the house my aunt had left us. That man was selfish, and I was more upset at myself that I had just sat there for years and allowed him to treat the kids and me like that. I also blame the Church because of they said for wives to submit to our husbands and he has the final decision and what he says goes. Something is seriously wrong with that thinking.

JANICE HYLTON-THOMPSON

Mama Was Wrong

*M*omma told me never to get rid of a man with an income. But what Momma forgot to tell me was that I would have to put up with a whole lot of crap. I'd have to sacrifice my self-worth, accept less than what I deserve, settle for a mediocre marriage, and put up with verbal abuse because he is the breadwinner.

I'm a clerk at the university, and we don't make that much above minimum wage. But I am working on my Bachelor's degree, which is free for me, so I'm not about to give up that job.

He says I need to start pulling my weight around the house and pay more toward expenses. He said I was worthless because I am an expense to him and not an asset. That made me feel so depressed and worthless.

My worth to him is the paycheck I bring home? I wash, cook, clean, fold up his drawers, clean up after him, sex him whenever and wherever he wants it, and tend to his every need. But I'm an expense and not an asset?

Submit?

*T*his whole submission discussion upsets me. Why should I submit to my husband, and how is he the head? He doesn't work, and he isn't even trying to find a job! But I'm supposed to submit to him?

My husband ain't no real man! My daddy is a real man! When my dad wasn't working, my daddy got a lawnmower and went from house to house asking people if they needed their lawn cut. And he brought my brothers along to show them what a real man does! While he was cutting the grass, they would wash people's cars for a few dollars.

A real man provides and protects his family! Ain't no real man gonna sit down and see his wife killing herself to take care of her family and not find a job! A real man doesn't make excuses like, "There's nothing in my field." Sometimes you have to do what you can do until better comes. I told him that all the fast food restaurants are hiring! He said that's beneath him!

I'm not submitting to a man who can't be *THE MAN*! Every evening I come home, he is sitting in front of the TV, playing video games, and eating my kids' food! If I submit to this man, we would be hungry, naked, and the bank would get the house! I can't let that happen to my babies! So much for marrying my college sweetheart who dropped out!

I always wanted a man like my daddy! Dad had told me not to marry him. He said, "Baby, don't marry a man who can't finish a job." But I was in love!

My husband ain't no man! He is still that little boy who dropped out of college because he was stressing! Talking about lots of people dropped out and made it! I asked him, "When are you going to make it? Because they weren't sitting at home doing nothing waiting for their wives to take care of them because they were lazy and didn't want to work."

Our 8-year-old son is more of a man than he is. At least, my baby boy comes out to the car and helps with bringing groceries into the house. Thank God my Daddy is still here to cut my grass and teach my baby boy how to be a real man!

I Don't Need a Man for His Money

I was a successful corporate American woman. But I wasn't meeting the type of man that I know I deserved, needed, and wanted. So, I settled for an aspiring rapper and DJ who was living with his brother. In no time we were married. We were both believers, and bought the cutest little house on a quiet street. He continued to pursue his music and DJing here and there, and I paid most, sometimes all, of the expenses.

We would have fights here and there about him finding consistent income, but it would always end with, "Baby, things are looking up."

Then we started having kids, and the market crashed. I was laid off, received unemployment, and used up all of our emergency funds. I did find another job paying me about 1/3 what I was making before, and that was just enough to put food on the table, health insurance, and buy the kids' school uniforms.

I used to say that I didn't need a man for his money! That's until my babies were bringing their toys to put in the moving truck because I couldn't pay the mortgage that I had worked so hard to keep for the kids.

I used to say that I didn't need a man for his money, until I saw how sad my babies were, crying that they were moving from their home that they were born in and had their own rooms, into a little apartment where all three of them would share a room. It was the only accommodation that I could afford without a credit check.

I used to say that I didn't need a man for his money until I realized that for 15 years, I had allowed my husband to sit home and not take on his husbandly duties and provide for us. Even when I lost my job, he didn't get up and get a consistent paying job. Even with the letters coming in the mail from the bank about the foreclosure, he would come to me and ask me what we were going to do and if I can get more hours at the job.

I used to say that I didn't need a man for his money until the kids and I needed his money and he didn't have any, nor would he get up and get a job to keep a roof over our heads.

THE NAKED WIFE

I used to say that I didn't need a man for his money until I lost all respect for my husband because the American dream that I worked so hard to provide for my kids was taken away from them. I used to say I didn't need a man for his money, but I am realizing now that I do need him for his money, in addition to all the benefits of a godly husband.

I Want
to Be......
S.E.X.E.D!!

The Weapon of Sex

I would never have thought that at my young and tender age I would be in a sexless marriage, all because my husband used sex as a weapon. If we got into an argument, he would withhold sex. If he felt like I wasn't affectionate enough, he would withhold sex.

The straw that broke the camel's back was when he returned from a weekend with his frat brothers. Sex came up, and he said to me, "Well if you learn to be nicer and more affectionate, you can get some sex." That felt like he took a sword and stabbed me right in my lower stomach where I had carried our baby for nine months.

I was so hurt that I packed a bag and went to a hotel, just to get my head together. Our marriage was already in trouble because of his infidelities, and I forgave him and went to counseling. I was trying to save our marriage, and yet, every chance he got, he seemed to tear me down, and not even try to work on or try to save our marriage.

You know it's funny, now that I think back because the sex wasn't even that good and I had to do all the work. But I just always remember the older church ladies telling us younger women to have sex with our husbands, regardless of whether we want to or feel like it or not! And, that's what I was trying to do.

JANICE HYLTON-THOMPSON

Frosty the Snowman has Frostbite

*M*y bedroom is so cold that if Frosty the snowman were in there, he would get frostbite. We have always had issues in the bedroom. Yes, even when we were dating and engaged there were issues.

My husband promised that he would work on it, but instead of it getting better, it got worse. Instead of him trying to work on or addressing it, he would act as if everything is okay.

Then there was a breakdown in our communication, where I was always the one trying to communicate, talk, spend time together, date, etc. I was always initiating, wanted to make him feel good about himself and telling him how much I wanted him and 'it.'

Then I got tired because everything was on me, and icicles have been growing in our bedroom ever since. And, I have no intention of warming it up. It is what it is!

To Be Pleased

*Y*ou know, I was listening to the guest preacher's message at the women's ministry, and I couldn't help but wish that my ex-husband was there to hear it. He was all about me pleasing him but not vice versa. It was always, "Honey get on top, get down." I was waiting for him to tell me to do him from behind.

When I asked can you do me, it was always, "Oh honey; I'm tired! You're the young one. You go to the gym four times per week. You have all the energy."

Yet, he refused to go to the gym and work out with me so that he could be healthier and have more energy!

I do not know what possessed me to marry a man who did not have an exercise ethic. But he told me that he would start going to the gym. That was just another lie he said to get me to marry him.

My Middle Name Is Sex

*S*ex is too important for me to have stayed in that marriage. He was older and didn't have a sex drive. I was younger, and my sex drive was on 100. I know what the Bible says about sex, and I waited for marriage, but it just doesn't work all the time. When you have waited your whole life and then marry someone who is all used up, over the hill, and worn out, and he is not able to hang, it is discouraging and frustrating.

And what makes it worse is that he doesn't want to do anything about it. So, what am I supposed to do? The First Lady said it was not about sex. Well, of course, she can say that! She has been with her husband for forty years. I was in the prime of my life, and there was no way I was going to stay in a marriage where my husband didn't want to have sex. Plus, I wanted to have babies, and how were we going to have babies if we weren't having sex?

In all fairness, I did try to stay and give him time to work on his issue, but he just didn't care. We went to the doctor who told him he needed to lose weight and work on lowering his cholesterol. A year later, he has done nothing. When he has a day off, he sits in front of the TV all day. In the meantime, I had set up a mini gym in the basement because I love to work out.

We went to talk to Pastor and his wife. The Pastor spoke to him separately, the First Lady spoke to me individually, and then the four of us spoke together. But in the end, I just couldn't settle for a sexless marriage. What's the sense of being married and not having sex? Isn't that one of the main benefits of marriage? Honey my middle name is sex!! Just go ahead and call me sex, because I can't live without it!! LOL!!

208

Have You Seen the Minute Man?

1, 2, 3, 4, 5… 18, 19, and 20! That's it! Imagine that is your sex life for 11 years? I'm not even sure how I got pregnant, but I guess that explains why we only have one child. You've heard of the Minuteman? Well, hold onto your hats, ladies — what about a 20-second Man? I think at this point; I would be glad for a Minuteman. We could have sex during a commercial break, be finished, and forget that we had sex!

You know what upsets me most of all? It is not so much that he only lasts 20 seconds; what upsets me is that he will not try to get any help. Won't go to the doctor, lose weight or exercise! So, for our 10th year anniversary, he came home with some Viagra, but there was no difference. Have you ever seen dogs have sex? Bam, bam, bam the end! That's it; that's my sex life.

It is so frustrating; it is driving me crazy. I'm to the point now that I don't even want to have sex with him! I am tired of getting all excited, thinking that something is going to happen, only to spend the next 20 minutes trying to get it up and it's just a waste of my time!

No romance, no intimacy, no calls or texts throughout the day. From the time he leaves for work in the morning until he comes home to flop down in front of the TV, I don't see or hear from him. At first, I would call, text, etc., but after years of no reciprocation, I have just stopped. I don't know how much more of this I can take. My youth and the sexual peak are just passing me by, waiting for this man to think about me and my needs. I suggested counseling, but he asked, "For what?"

Brains over Physicality

*M*y husband is a book, smart man. I am not physically attracted to him, and I had no passion or wanting to tear his clothes off when I saw him. At the time, I thought that the physical didn't matter. At least that's what the church ladies would say. Boy, did they lie! I guess their thinking is that women want security first, and then we will just deal with everything else.

But I'm finding out that I want to be attracted to my husband. When I see him naked, I would like to jump on him, and I don't. In all honesty, I never had any passion for him, I just kept on thinking he's a Christian and he has a great job, so passion doesn't matter. Not true!

I hate having sex with him. It freaks me out, and the closer he comes over to my side of the bed, the more I go over to the other side. One night, I fell off the bed. Now I have resorted to sleeping on the couch. It's like I'm having sex with my brother. In my mind, I'm thinking, "Please hurry up and finish." I just lay there! Gosh, that is so bad!

So, I went to see a counselor because I felt that something was wrong with me. Maybe I was raped as a child and forgot about it or something. She asked me if I have always been like that and I said no. I have had very healthy, loving, and passionate relationships before. We talked about my exes, etc.

She said everything is important in marriage. Many women think that a man's physicality doesn't matter, and they will grow to be attracted and desire them. However, the same way men want women to be attractive to them; women want their men to be attractive too.

And that it is important for each mate to be their best for their mates. Couples need to have physical attraction the way couples need to have similar spiritual backgrounds, financial compatibility, and so on. Couples who have similar experiences are the most successful. If you are like 'day' and he is like 'night,' and you are not able to meet at dusk or before the sunrise, you will never meet. Each person needs to care about the other person's needs and wants.

She also said I should not have married my husband; that we got married for the wrong reasons. She asked if I could see my husband humping on me for the next ten years and asked about having children. "Nope," I said and then she asked, "Then why did you marry him? "All of a sudden, everything made sense to me. Gosh, I don't even want to have babies for this man! Now that's sad!!

20 Years of Bad Sex!

*Y*ou heard me right!! Over twenty years of bad and awful sex!! We got married young and struggled to build a life together. The sex was just horrible from the beginning, and I was a virgin. People often say that's why we need to be virgins when we get married so that all we know is our husband. Please!! That's a lie!! You know when the sex is terrible, and he isn't exactly hitting the spot and putting your back out!! LOL!!

But for twenty years, I dealt with the bad sex. I often suggested we try different things, but he had no interest. Then I started having excuses why I didn't want to be bothered. I usually fell asleep in the kid's room but then they left for college, and it was just me and him and the bad sex.

Once I hit my sexual peak at around forty-two, there was no way I could stay with him. No, I can't say he has been unfaithful, or honestly, I didn't care where he was sticking his little ding-a-ling as long as it wasn't in me.

By the time we were married 20 years, we were living in separate parts of the house. And eventually, the marriage just fell apart. We divorced peacefully and split our assets evenly.

And now that I have experienced a real orgasm, I realize that I never had one while I was married!! I never knew my toes could curl and my eyes roll all the way to the back of my head. And I treasure my beautiful locks; I would have never thought I would pull them out!! Lol!!! Good sex is a gift from the Lord!!

THE NAKED WIFE

Momma Was Right

*M*y Momma told my sisters and me never to marry an old man. And what did I do? Marry an old man! My Daddy was almost twenty years older than my Momma. You know, in those days, parents would push the girls to marry older men because they were more established and could take care of a family. Even though my mother was born in the forties, she was more of a twenty-first-century woman.

She was very unhappy with my father, and always told us, girls, "Listen to me and listen well. Do not ever marry an old man. Marry a man who is in your age range, where you have things in common and grow together. Make sure you love each other. If you don't love him for him, don't marry him."

So, when I brought my husband to be home to meet Momma, she gave me one of those stares. When we were alone, she asked, "Baby, how old is he?"

When I said he was 48, she dropped the cup. My mom didn't smile the whole evening. Even at my wedding, she seemed so unhappy. She wasn't as involved as she was with my sisters' wedding. She didn't offer to help or anything. She just kept on asking if I was sure and I said, "Okay, Momma, so he is seventeen years my senior, but he doesn't look it."

"Baby, you just turned 31. What are you doing with a 48 -year-old man who is obviously going through his mid-life crisis and that's why he needs a young, sexy, and beautiful lady on his arm to make him feel good about himself? And what did I always tell you about a man with a huge gut or tire around his waist? Why don't you try to wait and meet someone who is more in your age group and have things in common with?

"Baby, I'm telling you right now. You are very active and have always been physical. You played basketball in college, for God's sake! Can't none of us keep up with you when we go hiking, and you think this old man can keep up with you in the bedroom?

Sweetie, it won't be long before you're having problems in the bedroom, that's if you haven't started having issues there already. That man is way too old for you. Don't you go rushing into marrying some old man because you think your biological clock is ticking? Wait on God, baby, wait on God. Now I'm not going to tell you what to do. You are an adult. You have done well for yourself, and I am very proud of you. But, baby, don't you marry that old man!"

"What about that nice young man you work with?" She asked!

I should have listened to what my Momma said. She knew what she was talking about. I have never in my life met a more stubborn man. He acts as if he resents me. Maybe I was his midlife crisis, and now his hormones have calmed down, and he realizes he has someone he needs to talk to, date, have sex with, and oh, have babies with!

I'm so ashamed; I can't even tell my Momma what's going on. But she's been asking for grandbabies, I'm the last of the girls, and I'm the only one that doesn't have any kids yet.

The truth is, there is no way I can have children with him. I would be a single parent, just as I am married but single. I'm in this marriage alone.

Cougar

ougar is my middle name! I have always loved younger men. I am 46, and men my age and older are so old-looking, unattractive, and lazy! And please let us not talk about those beer-bellies that hang off as if they are 12 months pregnant? Yuck, such turn-offs!

I have regretted not keeping my cougar ways. Years ago, it wasn't normal for older women to date or married a younger man. So, I went against what I wanted and married an older guy. Biggest mistake of my life! Except having my children, I have regretted that decision since I married him. I was 30, and he was 44. That was way too many years' difference, but to make my Daddy happy, I went ahead and married this older man who was established.

Those were the worst years of my life. He was just old! No energy, lazy, couldn't hold his own in the bedroom, and then he started to smell funny, like an old man. We just weren't compatible.

Now, people want to call me a cougar because I'm married to a younger man. He's not that much younger than me, I'm 46, and he's 40. But after being with an old man, I vowed never to even go to lunch with an older man.

And how is it okay for men to marry younger women, but if an older woman marries a younger man then she's a cougar? But, I must say I'm thrilled. He's just as energetic as I am. We work out together, run together, and have a lot of things in common. And most importantly, he talks to me! I did not know how much I was lacking and yearning for conversation until I met him! I just love a man that can talk to me.

And the SEX! I was missing out all those years. I remember asking my old husband just to grab me sometimes and throw me on the table and 'do' me. You know what he used to say? That his back hurts! Ugh! I was miserable, unhappy and unsatisfied! It was awful!

After the failure of my marriage, I am beginning to think that women should not marry men that are too much older. No more than seven years'

215

age difference. I don't believe that we should marry people we don't have things in common with and then hope that they will change.

Then the old fool started cheating! And that was my way out!

The Virgin Prostitute

I was practically a virgin when I got married. Got saved as a teenager, and stayed in the church and waited for God to bless me with my husband. Time went by, and I would meet different guys here and there, but nothing substantial. Then for a long time, I didn't meet anyone, and then I met my husband.

He started coming to the church and going out with us after church on Sundays and coming to different events. Eventually, he told me he was interested in me, and I said that I didn't feel the same way. He was much older than I like my guys to be, so that was an immediate turn-off. And I just wasn't attracted to him.

But, he kept pursuing me and hanging around the church, etc. Then the church mothers and my mom started pushing me to talk to him — "He's a good man, he's older, he's established, and so on." Then my friends got on the bandwagon, and so I decided to give him a chance. We weren't sexual or anything. We got engaged, and before I knew it, my Momma and aunties were planning the wedding, and the next thing I knew, I was married. It all happened so quickly.

Sex wasn't all that good. I was disappointed. Then we just stopped having sex, which was fine with me, because I didn't care to. But then, he would say little things like, "You can get some sex if you're nice to me." Or he would call and say he worked hard at work and he wanted to cuddle. I protested, and he went on to say that he was not gonna do all that stuff around the house and not get any cuddling. What did I think this was? So, I asked him what he thought this was?

For the first time in my life, I felt like a prostitute. He pays the rent and the bills, so whenever he is ready to have me, I needed to be available. But if I want to have some intimacy or anything like that, he flat out uses sex as a weapon. Can I tell you we only have sex when he wants to? Everything is when he wants it or on his terms. What kind of person is that? Is that the way it's supposed to be? Sex is only when he wants to?

Stolen Choice

*I*n counseling, questions were asked if we knew of any issues that could prevent us from being intimate or having children. I answered no that according to my knowledge I had no problems and could have children. Pastor asked him the same too — if everything was working — and he said yes.

We got married six months ago, and on the wedding night, I find out that he has issues getting and keeping an erection. I mean, it was as if I was beating a dead horse! We didn't have sex before we got married as we were both in the church and wanted to keep ourselves. 'Pissed' is not the word I want to use, but that sums it all up. I feel tricked, bamboozled, and that this is fraudulent.

Pastor says I should stick it through and do other things. Out of the six months of our marriage, we've only had sex two times and for less than a minute. I am pulling my hair out. I have stopped talking to him because he refuses to explain why he wasn't upfront and honest about his ED.

I feel as if my choice was stolen from me. I wasn't given an option in this. While dating and in marriage counseling, I asked if everything was okay there and he said yes. I'm sure some church folks are going to say, "What if he'd had an accident and it couldn't work?"

I think that's different! With an accident, I can understand that there will be problems, but when my choice is taken away from me, how do I live with that? What else is he hiding?

How can I stay with a man who lied and tricked me into marrying him knowing that his penis doesn't work? How do you face me knowing that you are a liar?

I Feel Dirty

I saved myself for marriage only to marry a man who doesn't seem interested in sex at all! He calls me a freak and that I'm too much, and that I want too much sex. I am in my mid-thirties. I am at the peak of my sexuality, and he tells me that he's not giving me any? I've suggested we go to counseling or a sexologist.

He makes me feel so dirty, and question myself and my desires. Once I asked him to pick up his stuff from the living room, and the next day when I tried to initiate, he said I was on punishment because I told him to pick up his stuff. Really?

How will we ever have children? You mean to tell me I waited all these years and kept myself for this? Can I say I regret waiting all those years for God to bless me with my husband?

Do you know how many opportunities I turned down, just to be obedient to God's Word? And now that I am married and should be having all the sex in the world, my husband is sex-shaming and punishing me?

Talk Dirty to Me

*W*here do I begin? I was practically a virgin when I got married. I was in the church all my life and messed up a few times, but after an abortion in college, I was determined to keep myself for the Lord and wait for him to send me my husband.

Well, finally at 28, God did! He was 35, so the age was perfect, and we had a lot in common. Or so I thought! From our wedding night, he was complaining about how loud I was being. I didn't understand how he wasn't excited. He didn't seem to be interested in sex. It was as if it was a chore, and I just didn't understand that.

I work out; I try to be soft, kind, gentle, dress sexy, you name it, I have done it to get this man to be interested in sex. The only thing left for me to do is to swing from the chandeliers!

One day, he was sitting on the couch, and I said something very provocative, and he just looked at me sideways. You would have thought that I had cursed or something. He called me over to him as if I was his little girl and said, "I married a beautiful church girl, and I want you to stay that way. Don't talk like that and don't you ever say that again. That's dirty talking!" I was at a loss for words after that!

Wives,
Submit to Your Husbands!

JANICE HYLTON-THOMPSON

A Submissive Wife

"*W*ives, submit to your husbands!" I would always hear at church, women's ministry, and read in books. I washed, cooked, cleaned, and sexed him whenever and however he wanted it. You name it, I did it, because I wanted to be a submissive wife.

But, I was so tired! The marriage was tiresome! It was as if it was a job I didn't like, that I couldn't stand to get up and go to every morning. But yet I continued to be a submissive wife. I worked a regular 9-5 and had to pick up children from school and daycare. Most evenings when I got home, he was already home watching TV, and dinner still needed to be cooked. Since he didn't like leftovers, I had to cook every night!

I still had homework to help kids with and to prepare everyone for school and work the next day. And he didn't want his clothes going to the cleaners. He wanted me to wash, starch, and iron everything by hand.

I hated my marriage, being married to him, and I honestly think I hated him. But yet I wanted to be a good, Christian, submissive wife.

The light came on for me when he suggested the unthinkable after I had birthed and nursed three of his children. During what I started calling 'my intimate chore' that "EXPLETIVE" indicated that we have a threesome with a twenty-something waitress who worked at his job. Something came over me, and I used words I haven't used since I was in high school.

How dare he disrespect me and our marriage like that when I have done everything in my power to please this man? I grabbed my kids and went to my Momma's house. I couldn't believe my Momma asked me if I had finally come to my senses and left him!

That night, once I put the kids to bed, I opened my Bible and read for myself about submission. What I was doing was not submitting. I was allowing him to control me, and I don't think that was what God intended.

40/40

I barely completed my Bachelor's degree because I got pregnant in my senior year and it was a high-risk pregnancy. I rushed to get married, and we have been married 17 years now, with three kids. I have always wanted to go back, but there was always something getting in my way. My husband would say, "Oh, not now, once the kids start school!" and then it was we couldn't afford it.

For my fortieth birthday, my Dad said he wanted to help me make my dream a reality. He wrote me a $40,000.00 check and told me to put it in a separate account and only to use it for school. My aunt, his sister, offered to watch the kids for the evenings I would be taking classes. He even offered to go with me to register and pick out my classes.

When I opened up that card and saw that 40K, I screamed and cried so hard. My husband grabbed the card and looked at it, and it was as if he turned into another person. He ripped up the check and the card. He went off, cussing, yelling and screaming how my Dad had disrespected him, and how he didn't want me to go back to school, and I needed to submit to him not wanting me to go back to school.

He went on saying things like he was the man of this house and family and he didn't expect me to go back to school, and I needed to stay home. "Why do you need to go back to school? You women with your degrees think that you are better than everyone else. Over my dead body will you go back to get some law degree!"

Something came over me, and I went off on him! I cannot write all that I said, but by the time I was finished, he was sitting on the couch like a little puppy dog. For 17 years, I had put up with his crap and the jealousy of me pursuing higher education and my family's few dollars. For years, I kept my distance from my family and dad because he was jealous of the relationship we had.

For years, I worked small dead-end jobs because he was uncomfortable with me making my own money. For years, I was the submissive wife, just doing what he wanted and not saying much, but on that night, I got my strength and my voice back! Timeout for the bull crap!

Barbie Doll

*M*y husband has always wanted me to look a certain way. I am all for fixing up myself, working out, looking, feeling, and being my best. I was never the 'makeup' girl, just as long as I had on some moisturizer, face-powder, and make-up for special occasions. It started as one thing — wear more makeup, add some hair, dye your hair, fake lashes, bleach skin, blond hair, liposuction, Botox, waist trainer, more Botox, breast implants, butt implants, etc.

After I had our son, I had gained a few pounds, and he suggested that I get a personal trainer, which I was okay with because I wanted to shed the pounds. I was lighter after the baby than I was before.

One day, I was in the bathroom brushing my 'blond hair,' and I think I heard him saying something about a rib. I asked him what he said, and he said he saw a show where doctors could remove a rib or two to make your waist smaller! I asked, "What did you say?"

And he said, "Baby, let's remove one or two of your ribs to make your waist smaller!"

The light came on for me! I looked in the mirror, and I didn't recognize myself. Breast implants, blond hair, fake eyelashes. I had sat back for ten years and allowed this man to turn me into Barbie! All because I was trying to be a submissive wife and make my husband happy!

My Husband is... a...

A Rapist

*R*aphael and I knew each other from High School. He was finer than divine wine. We hadn't seen each other in years but reconnected in 1999. We went out a few times and had a blast. I had just come back to the Lord, and he was a believer also. We both attended different churches. Honestly, I felt pressure from the church because we had started to date and then the church folks started with the "oh it's better to marry than to burn."

And full disclosure, I tried to get some, but he wasn't having it! He wanted to wait until we got married to have sex, as we had often talked about getting married. I was so impressed with that. He was a perfect gentleman, he opened doors, sent flowers and called regularly.

Whenever I needed him, he was there for me. He always made plans for us. Even though sometimes when I made plans to be with family and friends, he would make plans for us. I was a little suspicious, but I just let it go.

We started marriage counseling, and even my pastor was impressed with him. In 2000 we got married, and on our wedding night, he said he was tired, so we showered, had a cocktail and went to bed. I was ok with it, because it was a long day, plus we were married, and we could always have sex tomorrow.

Got into bed and the next thing I knew he grabbed me, held me down and ripped my lingerie and panties off and had me on my stomach. So, I thought, Ok, we hadn't done it yet, maybe he's just "hungry" but when I tried to turn over he pushed me down and said "don't "F" move!! I said, "hold on, I don't like this!!' He said, "shut the "F" and be still!!"

I was so shocked that I did what he said. All I know is that he should have been locked up for what he did to me that night. So, the next morning I asked him what the heck was that last night, and he just looked at me with the strangest eyes, smiled and walked out of the room.

I lived with that for three months, and I only remember two times where we didn't have rape sex. I hated night time, he didn't do it every night, but when he did, it was rape!! And when I was on my cycle, he would try to rape me in my rectum, but I would be so tense and afraid that he couldn't get through.

Finally, I got a restraining order and then a divorce. I am still traumatized to this day!!

Lazy

*M*y husband watches porn, and I know about it. At first, he denied it, but one day he left his computer on and our daughter got a hold of it. What was on it? Porn!

I texted him and told him that the baby has his computer, and he texted back and said, "Oh no, please take it away from her. I don't want her seeing what's on it." So, I asked him what's on it.

One evening, I came downstairs, and I asked him what he was doing. I knew he was watching it because he quickly changed the screen. So, I asked him why he preferred to watch porn than to work through our issues because we do have a lot of problems in the bedroom.

"I prefer porn than trying to work things out with you and having to work through all that stuff, and your attitude and stuff. It's just easier." He said.

My Punishment

I feel as if I have done something in my life that I'm paying for because my marriage has gone all wrong. You know, I saw the red flags and signs that I should not have married him, but I guess I was so desperate that I just overlooked them and hoped that he would change. I'm older than my husband, by twelve years to be exact.

He said and did all the right things. But about a year after we got married, he changed and became a different person. Never knew he had a temper! A terrible temper, where he throws and rips things apart.

He has thrown different things at me quite a few times. He has broken things that we've had to replace. I've had to spend the night at hotels a few times because I didn't feel safe. He has even said on a few occasions that he would kill me. I don't know this man that I am married to.

And, now I feel stuck because my family doesn't believe in divorce.

JANICE HYLTON-THOMPSON

A Great Dad

I hate to admit it, but my husband is a great dad. He is great with the kids. He is like Mary Poppins, Mrs. Doubtfire, and Belle all mixed up in one. Anything that has to do with the kids, he does it. Makes them pancakes, rolls around in the grass with the boys, dresses up like a princess for our daughter, let her polish his nails and put makeup and lipstick on him.

When they are sick, he stays up all night and rocks them to sleep, allows them to spend hours playing in the bathtub, you name it, he does it with them.

Unfortunately, he is a terrible husband. I honestly do not think he likes me. I think he just married me to have his kids because he does everything for them. Takes them to the doctor, goes to the schools, etc. He won't allow me to; he insists on going and doing.

One day, we got into a terrible argument because he treats me as if I don't exist. I blurted out that I was leaving, and he said, "You go ahead but leave my children!"

I can't stand him, and sometimes I feel as if I hate him, but just the thought of my babies not being around him breaks my heart. In 13 years, my little girl will be off to college, and then I will leave him if God doesn't work a miracle by then.

For now, I enjoy the joyful sounds of my babies' laughter while their Daddy throws them up in the air. The peace and comfort I see in their little eyes when they see his face every morning when they wake up. And the safety and love they feel at night when he tucks them into their beds.

My Struggle

*M*y whole marriage has been a struggle. It was a struggle while dating and engaged. Currently struggling while married! Honestly, I have just given up on the marriage. I even stopped sleeping in the bed with him. It's a struggle to get him to take a bath daily, especially when he's not going to work. Then he wants to come and hug me, and I'm just grossed out.

Yes, we all have a lazy day here and there, but going three and four days without washing? You know what I hate about struggling? It reminds me of the story in the Bible about Adam and Eve, how after they sinned, and God put them out of the garden and said they would eat by the sweat of their brow. Do you know what that is? Struggle!!

And please, let's not talk about sex. He is so freaking lazy in bed; it makes me sick!! For the first few years, I did all the work while he laid there on his back like a lump. I had to struggle for him to get up and do something!!

Getting pregnant was a struggle, but soon as I had my babies, I didn't bother with him anymore. I wanted to have another baby, but I just didn't have the strength to struggle with him. Staying in this marriage is a struggle. I am so tired and worn out from being married to him that I have given up on me too. I've been sleeping in the living room for the past three years now. We have a guest bedroom, but I'm so tired, and I don't want to move in there.

Everything about my marriage and husband is a struggle:

1. Talking to him
2. Listening to him
3. Looking at him
4. Dealing with him
5. Living with him
6. Getting him to take a bath

7. Getting him to brush his teeth

8. Getting him to change his funky clothes he's been wearing around the house for a while

9. Living under the same roof with him

10. Living is struggle

11. My life is a struggle

12. Honestly, I think I'm depressed because of how my life has turned out.

Struggle love is not sexy at all!! Please say "NO" struggle love and men!

Bachelor

I don't think my husband wanted to be married! I believe he met a beautiful girl who wasn't going to give up the cookies and I made my demands, and he knew that the only way to have me was to marry me! I always remember what my grandmamma said, "Why would a man buy the cow when he can get the milk for free?"

Unfortunately, that was all he did! Got married, and that's it! He still wants to control his money; I have no say! He takes care of his family while our home goes lacking! He doesn't want me in his space, in his things, changing the channel, nothing!

He doesn't want to talk or have sex or go to counseling. He doesn't want to take me to his office parties, work events, nothing. He doesn't wear his wedding ring; it's as if I'm a secret. Once we happened to be in the supermarket and we saw a friend of his, and he didn't even introduce me as his wife. Just as Melody.

Every so often, he packs his things and goes away for a week here and there. My husband is a bachelor and never became a husband. What husband acts and behaves the way he does?

JANICE HYLTON-THOMPSON

Old Man

For the life of me, I do not understand why these old men want a young woman but can't hang. Okay, yes, I had reservations about marrying a man who was almost 20 years my senior. I talked to him about it, and he assured me that he would work out and become healthy and do what he needed to do to make the marriage work, and keep the fire burning in the bedroom.

Well, for our first two years of marriage, if I didn't light the torch, there would have been no fire. And when I did, it wouldn't last at all. Being in the medical field, I would have never thought that a man in his 50s would have little to no sex drive at all.

And Viagra didn't help him either. I have a very high sex drive, so you can imagine how this drives me crazy. What's worse is that he doesn't care at all, which is just selfish of him. Men hit their peaks in their 20s and women hit our peaks in the mid-30s to 40s. At first, I questioned God about it. But from talking to my preacher friends, I realized that that was why couples needed to give and take and care for each other. If we are never at the same sex peak or drive, we both need to give and take.

Well for five years, I have been giving and getting nothing. The truth is, we haven't had sex in over a year. The fact that he doesn't even bother has caused so much tension and frustration that I don't want him touching me at all. All he wants to do is touch and grab my behind. And did I mention I want to have kids?

Every time I see a couple where the man is older than the woman, I just shake my head. These old men want to have a young woman on their arms but can't hold it up in the bedroom. They are over the mountain and are all sexed out while the young wives are burning with unquenched fire. So I am on a mission of telling young women that if sex is important to you, do not marry an old man because you will be pleasantly disappointed.

Did I stay with him? Heck no, I didn't stay with him! I am sorry. I was 37, and I hadn't signed up for a sexless marriage with no babies. Not! We were not having sex because it didn't work, and no sex meant no children and that was a no-no for me. Sorry!

I am now 40, and in a beautiful, full of sex marriage with a man of my age group. We have a baby on the way.

No, I was not fearful. I knew what I wanted and what I had was not what I wanted. I did try to work on it, but he had no interest, and that was not right for me. And I refused to live the rest of my life like that. I have worked very hard my whole life, and I saw marriage as a gift and a reward. But that was more of a punishment than a reward.

Old men need to marry women in their age group who are over the hill like they are, for whom sex once or twice a month is good. We younger wives need husbands who can handle us in the bedroom. Now, I know people have issues, like diabetes and high cholesterol, etc., and those were issues with my ex too. He never told me that he had those health problems because if he did, I would not have married him.

Why do you think old men don't get old women in their age group? Because they feel as if women their age can't put it down in the bedroom. These same old men want to get younger women who can put it down in the bedroom. And yet, they are not able to hang with the younger woman, and she ends up doing most of the work, while he tries to get his penis to work. Do you see the dilemma?

Like Father, Like Son

A man's ability to communicate with me has always been one of my requirements for me to date or continue to date him. He had to be able to stimulate my mind along with having intellectual conversations. To me, a man being able to communicate well was like him being born again.

When we were dating, he was always busy studying for his next lecture. Him being a professor intrigued me because I thought to myself, "Surely, he can communicate very well." But communication was always lacking in our relationship. Even when we were on dates, he didn't talk much. I had to be the one to initiate the conversation and ask questions.

One day while talking on the phone, I brought up his lack of communication and how it was vital for me to be with a man who will communicate with me, and not have me always trying to pull it out of him. He assured me that it wasn't an issue and would not be one when we get married.

He went on to say that his father never talked to his mother and that it made the marriage very difficult because she would want to talk when he got home, and he just wanted to sit and watch TV. I thought, "Oh, that's good! Then he will not repeat this mistake. He has experienced the same."

Wrong! His lack of communication has caused such tension in our marriage that we are currently living apart. It is puzzling to me that he has become like his father. When I bring up the story that he shared with me about his parents, he denies that he told me that.

We have gone to counseling, but nothing has changed with him. Then one day he said to me in the counselor's office that I am too needy. It brought tears to my eyes because all I want is for us to talk and apparently that is just too much for me to ask.

Truthfully, I don't see me staying in this marriage.

Secret Freak

I am afraid that I might have a secret freak on my hands. My husband is this prestigious, law-abiding, God-fearing lawyer who goes by the book in every situation.

That is until it comes to his extramarital affairs. He is conservative in the bedroom even though I wanted more!

One day, as I was packing his luggage for a "work weekend" while he was in the shower, a text message came on his phone. I picked up his phone, and there was a picture of a suitcase with all this stuff that looks like whips, chains, belts, feathers, handcuffs and other things I couldn't identify.

The text says, "wait till I get a hold of you this weekend!" As I look back on the messages, I was disgusted, shocked and pissed!! Something came over me, and I grabbed his belt, went to the bathroom, and I won't say what I did!?

Here I was a devoted, horney and unsatisfied wife in the bedroom and he's out there being a freak!!

Why wasn't he like that with me at home? I'm his wife, and I want him to tie me up and play with the feather and all that freaky stuff!! I want him to love me, enjoy me. Let me fulfill his sexual and most intimate desires. He should be telling me what he likes, and vice versa.

He would have been surprised if would had only taken some time to talk to me and explore.

I'm still here for now, while he begs and pleads for me not to pack the kids and me up and leave with more than half of everything! Plus, I quit my job!

A Whore

*M*y husband is a certified whore! I have had my suspicions, but nothing confirmed. We went to counseling, and he said he just needs to have more than one woman. He stated that there are too many women out there for any man just to be with one for the rest of his life.

I asked him why he asked me to marry him, and he said because he knew I was a good woman and I would make an excellent wife and mother. But I want to be in a monogamous marriage, and he said he couldn't be faithful to me.

Asked him why he didn't tell me before we got married, and he stated that I hadn't asked. I thought that was understood; that if you ask someone to marry you, then that means you are ready to be faithful to one woman?

I love him, our family, and our home. He is an excellent provider, and I don't want to lose him. What do I do at this point? This is not what I wanted!

Liar

*H*ave you ever seen the movie *Liar, Liar*? That's my husband. He lies for no apparent reason! I have never seen someone lie as much as he does.

He is so dishonest that I think he just can't help himself. Lying is so much in him and has become such a part of him that lies just come out of him. He hasn't attempted to work on the fact that he can't help but tell lies.

My husband makes excuses for everything. Every time he opens his mouth it's either a lie or an excuse.

I don't believe anything he says. If he says the house is on fire, I would roll over and go to sleep. Isn't that sad!?

Child

*M*y husband loves to say that I treat and talk to him like a child and that I need to respect him because he is a grown man! He loves to tell me how the Bible says for me to submit to him. See, my husband is a male, but he ain't no man!

Let's see what the Bible says about being a man. Paul said when I was a child, I acted like a child, but when I became a man, I put away childish things.

A man provides for his family, and if he doesn't have the job he likes right now, he will do what he needs to do (legally) to provide. Boys stay home with their mommas. He hasn't been working for God knows how long now. He can't hold a steady job and won't get any training to get a career. I begged my girlfriend to beg her husband to see if he could get my husband a job at the docks. He got him the job, and my boy-husband said it was too early for him to get up and be down there by 5 a.m. Is that the behavior of a man or a boy?

I must get up at 5 a.m. to be at work by 6, working two jobs to put a roof over our heads and food on my children's table. I asked him to make sure he gets the boys up by seven, so they can leave the house by 8:15 to get to school around the corner by 8:30, but he can't get up to do that. Thank God for my momma who comes by every morning on her way to work to wake them up and drop them off. Is that the behavior of a man or a boy?

I have asked him that since he is home and I'm working two jobs if he could clean up, cook and wash. He said he ain't doing that because that's a woman's job. So, I told him since that's a woman's job, I will quit my two jobs so I can stay home and do women's work. Is that the behavior of a man or a boy?

Then I asked him to help the boys with their homework so that when I get home it's already done, but instead he half does it. So then, I had to get a tutor to come to the house every evening to help the boys with their homework. Is that the behavior of a man or a boy?

When it was back-to-school time, I brought the kids to buy sneakers. He went and picked up some $300 sneakers, and when we got to the cashier, I only paid for the kids. You know what he did? Had a tantrum! I was so embarrassed! And he yelled, "That's our money!"

"Our?" I asked! "It's our money when you go and work for it! Remember, you couldn't get up that early, so you don't have any money!" Is that the behavior of a man or a boy?

Therefore, since he acts like my brother used to act when we were kids, I guess that makes me his momma, and he is one of the boys, who are 8 and ten but are more men than their daddy.

So, he wants me to stop treating him like a kid? Fine! Grow up and be a man. If he wants me to respect him, he needs to earn it. So much for getting with a brotha down on his luck with a little bit of potential!

A Drunk

For years, I was mad at my husband because he was a drunk. And then I thought back to the first time I had seen him drunk. It was September 19th. We were dating and not engaged yet. That date just stuck in my head because I was disgusted with him.

He was so drunk that he couldn't walk straight. Thank God, his brother was with us and helped him home. That night he was like a child with no control. His decision-making was off. He wanted to take a cab from one state to another; it was just awful. I was so shocked that I just sat there.

The next day I had a serious conversation with him. I told him the story of my father being a drunk, and how I vowed never to date or marry a drunk. He listened and said it wouldn't happen again.

But two months later, we went to a dinner party, and once again he got drunk out of his mind. He turned into someone else, he looked different and talked differently, and I didn't like who he was.

Once again, I had a serious conversation with him, and again, he gave me the same lame promises. A year later, we wed, and six years later, I am still dealing with the drunk. I am so drained and worried. But, the truth is, I have to take responsibility. I overlooked the red flag and married him.

Now I'm pissed at myself for marrying a drunk. Hard-working, a great guy, and dad, when not drunk. I guess I just weighed it in my head. But honestly, I'm tired of dealing with his drunken ways and temper, and I just don't have it in me anymore to deal with it. It has gotten worse over the years.

Teen

*M*y husband is a toddler and teen all wrapped up in one! A man who I need to tell to brush his teeth, take a bath, change his dirty, funky clothes he has been wearing all week is not a man who needs to be married. At least not to me! But that is who I am married to.

I don't know if his momma didn't teach him, but I am so disgusted! And then he wants to cuddle up to me with his funky breath, body, and clothes?

I went to talk to my Pastor who said I could work through that. How do you work through a forty-six-year-old man not keeping up his hygiene? I have been trying to work through it for the two years of our marriage, and it's been the same. How do I respect that, look up to him? I just see disgust when I look at him.

On my days off, I am so tired because I spend my time picking up after him. This last time when he left his drawers on the floor, I put them in the garbage. Every time he left them on the floor instead of putting them in the hamper that is right at his feet, I put them in the trash until he didn't have any drawers left.

When he asked where his drawers were and why he didn't have any clean ones, I asked him if he had put them in the hamper. He said, "Nope, I left them on the floor." I told him that anything on the floor is garbage.

He went off cussing and quarreling, asking what kind of wife I was, I was supposed to pick up after him and he ain't got no clean drawers. I told him that I wasn't his maid.

So yeah, this is not going to work out. I'm too old for this foolishness!

Toddler

$\mathcal{P}$icture a toddler having a tantrum! That's my husband! When he doesn't get his way, he throws things, falls out, pushing over couches, chairs, practically crying and talking in a baby voice, folding his hands and pouting! I am so afraid that he will have a tantrum when we are out somewhere that I have stopped going anywhere with him.

Yes, he had little habits while we were dating, but we would talk through it. Plus, we didn't live together before we got married, and you know the saying, 'You don't know a person until you live with them.' I am not advocating shacking up, but something needs to be done so we can know how each other live and behave under pressure.

It is scary being with a man who behaves like a toddler! He refuses to go to counseling and blames me for causing him to act like that. I knew it was over when we argued, and he turned into the Hulk, flipped the couch over, and walked out. I grabbed our son who was cowering in the corner.

A few days later, my real toddler, who was 18 months old, was having a tantrum and he flipped over his little table! That was when I realized he was a bad example to our son, and I could not allow that to happen.

My husband is spoiled rotten, and I do not need that in my life! I want an adult man as a husband, not a little toddler.

JANICE HYLTON-THOMPSON

Negotiator

$\mathcal{M}$y husband is senior negotiator! He negotiates everything from helping around the house, sex, how much he will put towards monthly expenses, helping with the kids, putting gas in the car, everything!

After 17 years, I got tired of it. It was as if I had four kids instead of three. He has always been a negotiator, and at first, it was cute when we were in college, but at 37, I just got tired of it.

My breaking point was when I needed to go back to school for about six months to get a certificate so that I could move up in my job. I needed him to pick up the kids from school and do homework. I always had dinner prepared, so all he needed to do was warm it up. He told me no because when he wanted to go to his homecoming with his boys, I wouldn't help him buy the ticket and the hotel.

My mouth practically hit the floor in disbelief! I couldn't believe it! "So, let me get this straight," I said to him. "First, you don't make enough money to take care of the household expenses. I have been pretty much carrying this family by myself for years for the kids, and you are mad because paying the mortgage is more important than you hanging out with your boys for a weekend?

"I am trying to go back to school so that I can make more money, and you won't help with your children? Everything is on me. I haven't been able to make any deposit to the kid's college fund in about a year, and you are refusing to help?"

"I didn't want all of those kids, you did!" he said.

Right then and there, I broke down!

My Project

I feel as if my husband is my project. A building that I am building and fixing up that never gets completed. A build a man that never get to mature place. I married him a year after he got out of jail with a felony conviction.

My project had started coming to church, and he was a nice guy. Had a hard time getting and keeping a job. I helped him to find work and somewhere to live, but finally moved him in with me before we got married, without the church's knowledge of course. Big mistake!

Couldn't keep a job, so all the bills were on me. He couldn't have a license, so I had to drive him everywhere. He just always had problems, there was always something wrong with him. Once, he started to hang back in the streets. It was as if he was a teen that I had to stay on top of. I would leave work at lunchtime to drive by the house to see if he was hanging out or looking for a job.

It was so much with him that telling you this story is exhausting. He sucked the living life out of me; I had nothing left. I gave him my all in all, and yet and still, it wasn't enough.

JANICE HYLTON-THOMPSON

Let the Older Women Teach the Younger Women

First Lady Counsel

*M*arriages back then were different. My Daddy and Paul's daddy stayed on him about being a praying man first, a good husband, and father. On Saturdays, it would be the three preachers on our porch going over the Bible and preaching to each other. Every Saturday, we had an audience because Daddy would be out there preaching.

Over the years, we have had some tough times, but I have never wanted to leave. I cannot say that my husband has been unfaithful. He traveled a lot as a young preacher, and even today he still does. Back then, I had the kids and couldn't travel as much, but today I go most places with him.

Men were different back then. God, Bible, keeping your family together, and making your wife happy was necessary. Most of the time, we didn't have much but each other. And, back then, women put up with a lot of things because he was the breadwinner. Some husbands would be cheating, and yet women had to stay with them. Not because they wanted to, but because they had no choice. The same thing applied to abuse — women stayed and many lost their lives because they didn't have a way out or any means to support themselves and their children.

Men today are different. They behave as if they have something wrong with them. I see it with my son and my sons-in-law. Also with the men that come for premarital and marriage counseling. Somewhere, something has happened! I don't know if it's the milk or the food, but something has happened with our men.

Men today treat their wives like a new toy. They get used to it and then they want to discard them for a new one. And usually, it's the wives that are fighting to save their marriages because they love their husbands and will do anything to save their marriages. I see it every day!

I know that my daughter-in-law is going through this with my son, even though he comes from a good Christian home, mother, and father intact. We tried hard never to argue in front of the children. We raised him to get married and be faithful, but he just doesn't seem to want to grow up and be a responsible husband! I try to encourage her and tell her to hang in there and hold on and to pray for him. I would never tell her to leave or stay. That's a decision for her to make.

My husband has talked to Paul Jr. about him being a better husband. Love your wife, support her, be faithful, do right by her, help her with the kids, bring her flowers, etc. And my daughters, they're going through this, too, and are fighting to save their marriages. These men today don't want to be men.

Of course, not all men are like that, but as the first lady in a church that conducts hundreds of weddings, the common factor is that these men today don't want to grow up. They want to act like little boys with a new toy until they get used to it.

It saddens me because I have one girl left to be married and she is in her thirties and has yet to meet a suitable husband for her. Many wives come in to talk to me, crying about their marriages and their husbands. It breaks my heart!

As a first lady, except abuse, I encourage wives to try and work the marriage out. I have seen many couples overcome infidelity and gone on to have a happy and lasting marriage. But, it takes work! He's going to have to change his ways. Check in with her, no secrets, no secret Facebook or Instagram accounts. If you have a lock on your phone, your wife should have the password! There should be no secrets between a husband and a wife, especially if he has been unfaithful and she is willing to work to save your marriage.

When husbands mess up, they should be humble about getting right! Don't expect her just to move on! Give her time and space to heal. Listen to your wife, talk to her, and understand her! Men don't take the time to talk to their wives today.

We encourage both husbands and wives to get into counseling when there has been an injury to the marriage. Get into men's and women's fellowship. One thing I love about my Paul is that, no matter how tired he is, he takes time every day to talk to me.

And let me give you this extra little tidbit. We have been married for over forty years, and our bedroom is still on fire! See, when both people care about each other and about fulfilling each other's needs, you will make it happen.

I don't understand when couples come into marriage counseling and say that it has been two and three years since they have had sex? And these are young couples. Not old folks like Pastor and me!

How does a husband have issues with sex and not try to address it to meet the needs of his wife? How do you not try everything possible to satisfy your wife? I don't understand that. What Bible are they reading? That is being selfish!

And these are church folks I'm talking about, not worldly people! I don't understand it! The number of wives that come into my office to speak of a sexless life is puzzling to me. Because when my husband and I were coming up, we had so much sex that I'm surprised we don't have 50 kids! We only have five!

When God brings a man and woman together in Holy Matrimony, it is because they had a need that each can fulfill. A husband is to protect his wife, provide for her, and profess his undying love. Love, treasure, and cherish her. Don't compare your wife's body to another woman's. Your wife has borne your children!

A husband has to focus on his wife and seek everyday ways to put a smile on her face! At least, that's what my Paul does. I remember one day I was so upset with him, for what I don't remember. But, what I remember is Paul going outside and pulling up some flowers out of my garden and bringing them to me. I couldn't help but burst out laughing. That is what a husband is supposed to do. Keep his wife, happy, satisfied, fulfilled, and smiling.

Woman Pastor
Pastoring for Over 30 Years

One of the biggest mistakes I made in my first marriage was marrying a man who was not spiritually mature. It resulted in him not knowing or understanding that he was the head. Marrying a man who does not understand that he is the head, and one who cannot lead, is like driving an 18-wheeler tractor-trailer yourself without depending on your husband to drive it.

Someone who cannot drive it, probably can't even start it. If he starts it and tries to drive it, it will only cause disasters, casualties, and maybe even death. But even though we know they can't be our head, we marry them while thinking we can help them and show them how to be the head.

I made that mistake as a young woman and a minister. I wanted to be married and have a family so badly that I overlooked many red flags. My husband had a good heart, but he was a weak man. The children and I endured a lot of abuse and neglect and had to go without because he put his extended family before us.

It caused a lot of tension, strain, anger, animosity, and resentment on my end because I was working like a field animal, and the more I worked, the less the kids and I had. He couldn't say "no" to them but could say "no" to the children and me.

I was sick for about a month and couldn't work. We did not have any savings either. And then the downward spiral began. Have you heard the saying that most families are just one paycheck away from being homeless? That was us. The one month I was sick affected everything, and that was when I decided that I couldn't do it anymore. I realized that I needed to be about my children and me. We were evicted from our home, and I was able to move in with my parents, and he moved in with his family.

In a year, I was out of debt, which was not a lot but because I was using my credit cards to make ends meet. They were all maxed out though. I paid

250

off my credit cards, saved three months of emergency fund, and saved enough money for the kids and myself to move into a lovely apartment in a better city, which meant better schools. I also filed for divorce which was the best decision for us.

A few years later, God blessed me with a wonderful husband. He is a true man of God who is filled with the Holy Ghost and is in submission to God. When I tell you I have no concerns, all of my needs are met, I mean it. He is a provider and protector. I don't worry about a single thing because I know that my God-ordained husband has got it!

He loves my babies as his very own. God blessed us with another beautiful little boy whom we named "Joshua." He is such a joy and a reminder that God's Word is true. He's the last one to be going off to college soon. When I was going through my divorce, the Lord had said that he would renew my years like the eagles and that I would redeem the years that were stolen from me. God has done that for me, and I am so grateful!

This is My Counsel as a Pastor for over 30 Years

The reasons why marriages fail are innumerable because they vary for different couples. There are some things that one person is willing to deal with that another person is not. One thing I have noticed in over 30 years in the ministry is that if the "head" is not right and is out of order, nothing else will be right. If a husband is not able to lead his family and be an example, the family will suffer, and the marriage will most likely end in divorce.

Unless, of course, the wife takes on the leadership role and leads, but she will then be very stressed and exhausted because God did not create women to be the head. I am not talking about a mom who is a single parent.

Of course, she must head the household, but even then, it will become stressful for her.

In a marriage, the husband is responsible for the direction in which the family goes. Many wives try to maintain the family by trying to be the head, spiritual leader, provider and protector, even when there is a man in the home. The wife recognizes that if she doesn't take on the leadership role of her family, they will suffer further.

Therefore, this is my counsel: It is crucial for women, and especially women of God, not to marry men who are not men of God and who do not know who they are in God. Some women, including myself, married men who said that they were saved. However, that was it. They just accepted Jesus and never grew from that.

Women should not marry men who do not know who they are of God and then try to tell them who they are, especially if they are not able to understand. Why? Because some men of today were raised by single women and there was a not a father, or a father figure to teach them how to be men or a husband. I know a lot of women say they can teach their sons to be a man, but they are wrong. A woman cannot teach a boy-child how to be a man because she is not a man!

For a man who has not been fathered, when he gets married, unless he has done some reading, or teaching or counseling, he will not know how to be a good husband. This, explains his inability to walk in his God-ordained role, birth irritation, frustration, resentment, bitterness, anger, and the like on our part, but rebellion on his wife's part.

My father used to say that we can bring a mule to a bucket of water, but we cannot make him drink it. Because we know the capabilities of our man, if they can't or don't want to see it and apply themselves to the Word of God, they will end up hating and hurting us. God created men to be the head, but many are not walking in the power and authority that God has given them. Many do not understand the anointing that being the head carries.

Some women, and typically Christian women marry men who do not know what it means to be the head of his family. Some of us, including me, get weary of waiting. Our clocks begin to tick, and we listen to what the church-mothers tell us, which is to marry men who have potential, but we need to stop that. We need to stop marrying men who we know are not able to be the head and lead, cover, protect, and provide for us.

Christian women need King David. He was not afraid to be the head and lead his army in battle! With all of its beautiful rewards, marriage is also a battle. As women of God, we need a man who knows who he is and can be the watchman on the wall. We need a man who is in submission to God, praying, fasting, studying God's Word, and seeking His face, and who can go before God for his wife and family!

Women of God need to stop marrying men to help them to become what we want them to be. No, that is backward. Only a mother is supposed to prepare a man-child. If you are a woman of God, and you are trying to make your man equipped for you, you will have a headache. We need to stop marrying men with potential.

Stop marrying males who are not men! Stop marrying males who do not know who they are. Stop marrying men who are not able to provide for our children and us. See, a real man of God who has been fathered knows that God created him to be the head of his family. A woman does not have to convince a true man of God that he must be the head.

Stop marrying men who don't know who they are in God, and therefore are not secure in who they are in God. Stop marrying males who are looking for someone to tell them who they are. My father said that it is better not to marry than to marry a fool. Lots of women are married to idiots! And the sad thing is that you knew he was a fool before you married him. WE NEED TO STOP IT!

When I was coming up, without telling my age, men used to jump through hoops to try to marry us. Men use to pursue us and come to meet our daddies. These days, women are jumping through hoops to convince a man that she is marriage material.

Some women are taking care of men and moving them in their homes to try and show them that they can be wives. We need to stop it! Some women are moving such men in with their children, and they don't even know who he is. Red flag! If he must move in with you because he can't afford his own place, he is not a man! He is a child!

As women of God, we need to get back to doing things God's way. We allow men to be children because we are busy mothering them and teaching them how to be men! For the short time that I was a single mom, my father would come to my house several times per week and spend time talking to the kids.

Daddy would tell me, "Sweetie, you can't raise a boy to be a man because he needs a man to show him how to be a man. Only a man can teach a male child how to be a man." As women, we can't teach our sons how to be men, so why do we take up adult males who are not men and try to teach them how to be men so that they can be the man and husband that we desire?

As women of God, we need to stop it! You knew he was a fool when you married them. You knew he was abusive, a cheater, controlling, wasn't saved, didn't have a job, wasn't able to be your head, but you hoped that he would change and become the man you prayed for and needed. You knew he was a fool when you married him and hoped that you could turn him into a wise man!

Wisdom comes from God and God alone and if he hasn't gone to God to find out who he is, then may God help you. Because your life will be one of chaos and heartache and you will spend your entire marriage trying to make him into who you need and to be the King you need. Think about it!

Wait on God my sisters. Please pay attention to the red flags!

The Marriage Counselor

*P*eople are always so quick to say how marriages lasted longer 50 years. Can we, please have a real conversation about the truth though? Yes, some marriages worked years ago, and they lasted longer, but the fact is that many wives stayed because they didn't have a choice. The man was the sole provider, and the wife stayed home and took care of kids and home.

Many husbands were abusive. They cheated and had other families in the streets, but the wives stayed. Why? Because she didn't have a choice. The husband was the provider, and the wife depended on him for everything. If she picked up and left because of abuse or adultery or ill-treatment, she didn't have anywhere to go. Or, she couldn't provide for herself and kids. So many wives stayed and dealt with it because they had to.

And that's what the Church folks wanted to tell me when I packed up all six of my children and left my husband the elder. No, ma'am, I refused to deal with abuse and adultery! Those are two things that I will not tolerate. Yes, couples go through disagreements, but those things can be worked out. But abuse and adultery? Absolutely not!

I had a couple who came to see me recently. The wife has been trying to get him to go to counseling for the longest possible time. She finally gave him an ultimatum and, so he came. The first thing he said was that his parents had been married for 55 years, and so he didn't understand why his wife was talking about counseling and wanting to leave him. "That is a long time," I said and complimented him. But as the discussion went on, I came to find out that his father had left home when my client was three, has been shacking up for 44 years. My client is now 47.

WAIT ONE SECOND! Your dad has been shacking up with another woman for 44 years while he is still married to your mom and you want to sit up here and tell your wife and me that your parents have been married for 55 years??

"Yea, but he has finally come home," he said. "My mother is a woman of faith and prayer, and for 44 years she has been praying for him. Now that's a good woman and a good wife. She's not like these new wives these days. You have a little disagreement, and they are ready to leave."

"Sir, you are abusive to your wife and children. You call that a little disagreement? Anyway, what happened that he came back? Is he sick, did she leave him, what was it?"

"Well, he is sick, and his kidneys are going. You know, from the drinking."

"So, he came home because he was sick?"

"Yea, but he still provided for us and all."

That's just one example of how people blow the trumpet that they have been married for 50 years, regardless that it is full of dysfunction inside. So, when I hear people say that marriages worked better back then, I just drop my glasses and looked at them. And ask them to explain.

The truth is that marriages didn't work better back then any more than they do today, but that women back then depended a lot more on their husbands. These days, most women have their own money and can provide for themselves and their children. That is the reason why we are not putting up with all the bull crap.

Sweetie, I have been a marriage counselor for 20 years and still going on strong. I could tell you stories for days. And the only difference between couples that have been married for 50 years and couples today that has been married for only five years is money. I wouldn't encourage any woman to waste her time with a man who is not doing right by her.

Look at me. After having seven babies for my husband, I quit my government job that paid me quite well because we had five girls and he wanted to continue to try for a boy. He started acting like a fool; the fights happened more and more. Then I got pregnant again and had Hannah. He refused to add her to his insurance, and I had to go and get on government assistance so that I could take my baby to the doctor.

But that was okay. I put him on child support where I was getting $2500 per month. And, Thank God I had my degree to fall back on. I started counseling online and over the phone. I made ends meet, and my babies and I did well. I refuse to put up with foolishness from a grown man. And we were high school sweethearts, so he wasn't just some man I had met on the street. We were married for almost 20 years when he started giving me and his kids his 'behind' to kiss.

And I refused to deal with it. Why? I had seen my mom and all the ladies at the Church putting up with and dealing with foolishness from their husbands. He would be gone, and she would be at the altar praying for him to come back home. I didn't pray one prayer for that idiot. Either you want to be married and be a good father, or you don't. He didn't, and so I gave him his walking papers.

Now my mom lives with me, still praying for daddy to come home.

Conclusion

*C*ongratulations!! You have completed *The Naked Wife!* Were you touched and moved the way I was as I read it over again? As I mentioned in the introduction, I will not give a rebuttal. The Lord gave me this book as a platform for my Sistas, to tell their stories. I will forever be grateful to the Lord for using me and to my Sistas who trusted me to tell their many stories.

On to the conclusion then;

Take 1, 2, 3, 4, 5, 6, 7 and action! Yes, this is conclusion number 7, written about eight months after I completed *The Naked Wife*. You can read conclusion number 6 on my blog at www.janicehyltonblog.com entitled: *"Are You the Naked Wife?"*

I wasn't pleased with that conclusion either. And my editor thought that I needed to do a little more. He stated that being the author, I had authority on the subject and I needed to write in that authority. I thought that was a cool idea. So, I decided to think and pray about it some more.

One day as I was playing with my baby, the Lord reminded me of a woman in the Bible, known as "A Certain Woman." It's one of my favorite stories, I have taught and written about it on several occasions because there is just so much in it.

So, here goes conclusion #7 of *The Naked Wife*:

As I completed *The Naked Wife*, I realized that I was somewhat living in a bubble my whole life, about marriage. And at this conclusion, I'm ready to admit that my views, idea of marriage, was perhaps to some extent, that of a fairy tale. Yes, I know that every marriage goes through and experience tough times. However, I was under the assumption that if you love your spouse, then you will fight.

Even though I was a teen mom at 16 years old, I was very naive. Thankfully, I met my spiritual father and mother, Pastor/Bishop Marvin Bradshaw Sr. and First Lady Edna Bradshaw when I was 17 years old. They took me under their wings and taught me the word of the Lord and how to apply it to my life.

Pastor Bradshaw (back then) taught me that I needed to turn from the direction I was going in and to honor the Lord in my body and life. Additionally, that I needed to raise my baby girl, Alexia, in the ways of the Lord. Pastor Bradshaw told me that men only wanted what was between my legs and that I didn't need that. But that I needed to begin to pray for the Lord to bless me with my husband. And, that's why I have always wanted to get married. LOL!!! (Read more in my book for singles, coming soon.)

My spiritual father had given me the tools I needed to understand what men mean when they say "A," but means "B." As a teen mom, he sat me down and told me how beautiful and unique I was. That I needed to love, honor and respect myself. He told me that all men want to have sex, but I didn't need that, but I needed a husband.

Father, taught me that my body was the temple of God and I should not allow different men in my body like a hotel. But to wait on God for my husband, because if I allowed it, men would only "screw" me and leave me. BUT, if I wanted to be married to wait on God and listen to him.

Pastor Bradshaw told me that husbands were to profess their love, provide and protect their wives. So, as a single woman, that's what I did. I always thought/knew that I would be married by the time I graduated college, but I wasn't. So, at twenty-four years old, I stopped dating because I had not met who and what I wanted in a husband. (Read more in my singles book, coming soon.)

I had my list of what I wanted in a husband, and I refused to settle for anything less than what I wanted. So, I began to pray more intensely and specifically, for God to bless me with my "Boaz." I prayed for a husband that I could work because I wanted to, not because I had to. I prayed for a husband who would love me and my daughter and one that would honor me as his wife and take care of me. I prayed for a husband that would never lay his hand on my daughter or me to abuse us. I prayed for a faithful husband, but most importantly a true man of God.

259

So, it is no wonder I was shocked as my Sistas, many of them were my Sisters in the Lord, that were telling me stories of abuse, abandonment, adultery, and abuse of power. I was shocked that many husbands were looking for someone to provide for them versus providing for their wives. Pastor Bradshaw always told me to be on the lookout for men who wanted a place to live. Thus, attaching themselves to women who had a "little something."

Pastor Bradshaw told me that my husband was to love, protect and treat me like the queen I am. My husband is to be a man of God, faithful, hold my hand, open the doors, pull out my chair and send me flowers. He said a good husband is one that helps his wife around the house and so on.

The pastor said both husband and wife are to submit to each other and love each other. Husbands are to lead, be the head and set examples for their wives and children. Husbands are the watchmen on the walls of their home. Husbands are to love their wives like Christ loves the Church. And daddy would end by asking "How did Christ love the Church? He died for her!!" Husbands are to sacrifice their lives for their wives!

Yes, yes, I know there is no man, woman or marriage that is perfect or is without trials, testing, and tribulations. Another thing Pastor Bradshaw would say is that every couple will face a storm in their marriage. But, pray that you get your storm early in your marriage because early in your marriage you are still or should still passionately be in love.

Therefore, as I completed *The Naked Wife*, I was in disbelief at many of the stories because, in my mind, husbands are to love their wives, as Christ loves the Church. But, especially for my Christian sisters, their stores were an eye-opener for me and shocking!! Many of their fairy tales and my ideas of marriage had turned into a nightmare. And for a New York second, everything Pastor Bradshaw told me about how a husband is to treat his wife, was in the balance. But God!!

It is with this that I look to the precious Word of the Lord for a word of encouragement for my Sistas, and all of *The Naked Wives*. And within the word of the Lord, is one of my favorite story, about A Certain Woman.

Dear Naked Wife/Woman

There are times in our lives where we will or have gone through some "stuff," that will shake the very foundation of our faith. Jesus calls these "stuff" tribulations in **John 16:33**. However, Jesus also said that He had overcome the world.

Those "stuff" can cause some heart and soul issues. Some things affect us so deep that the Bible calls them iniquities. So that means there are some experiences that we can experience that goes all the way deep down to our bones. Some people have caused our hearts and souls so much pain, hurt, anger, disappointments, and resentments that it will take God himself to free us from those heart and soul issues. Some experiences will cause us to feel that not only have our loved ones left us, but God has left and abandoned us.

But, in **Isaiah 43**, it talks about how God will be with you through the fire and the flood. That means, no matter what we go through, God will be there. **Psalm 139,** talks about even if we make our bed in hell or fly to the uttermost parts of the world, God is there.

Therefore, God our father is letting us know that no matter where we go, what situation we get ourselves in, He will always be there for us. There might even be sometimes where we feel that God is not there. Or, we might ask "God, where are you?" Know that God is always present and available to help and hear our cry.

The Naked Wife is filled with the stories of my Sista wives who have experienced some trials, tribulations, disappointments, regrets, frustrations, abuse and even some questionable circumstances. Allow me to speak to your hearts, spirits, emotions, souls, your royalty and identity!

You were faced with various issues because your husbands that asked your father or you for your hand in marriage had failed you. Your husband who stood before God's holy altar, took vows and signed a contract to profess his love, provide for and protect you, but instead have left you destitute and NAKED!

BUT, GOD YOUR FATHER HAS COVERED YOU!

261

A Certain Woman

Allow me to speak a word of encouragement to you from the story of "A Certain Woman." You can find her story in **Mark 5:25-34** and I will add it here just in case you are not familiar with it. It reads:

25 And a certain woman, which had an issue of blood twelve years, 26 And had suffered many things of many physicians, and had spent all that she had, and was nothing bettered, but rather grew worse,

27 When she had heard of Jesus, came in the press behind, and touched his garment. 28 For she said If I may touch but his clothes, I shall be whole. 29 And straightway the fountain of her blood was dried up, and she felt in her body that she was healed of that plague.

30 And Jesus, immediately knowing in himself that virtue had gone out of him, turned him about in the press, and said, Who touched my clothes?

31 And his disciples said unto him, Thou seest the multitude thronging thee, and sayest thou, Who touched me? 32 And he looked round about to see her that had done this thing.

33 But the woman fearing and trembling, knowing what was done in her, came and fell down before him, and told him all the truth. 34 And he said unto her, Daughter, thy faith hath made thee whole; go in peace and be whole of thy plague.

This "Certain Woman" issue had broken her spirit. It had affected her emotionally, spiritually, psychologically, financially, health wise and socially! You, my sistas, because of your "issues" have been affected like this Certain Woman. And I submit to you, that like you, this Certain Woman was a naked woman!

When we look at the story of "A CERTAIN WOMAN" there are a few things that stand out.

The Bible does not give her name or state if (she) was:

1. jew or gentile
2. rich or poor
3. married or single
4. had a family, husband or children

5. short, tall, fat, skinny, pretty or ugly
6. what color her hair was.

Why? Because when you have an issue that only Jesus can fix, none of that matters!

Despite the Bible not describing this "Certain Woman," let us assume she was Jewish. You see, in the Bible days, whenever a woman was on her cycle she had to be separated. You can read more in **Leviticus 15:19-28.**

This Certain Woman had an issue of blood for twelve long years.

1. Ladies, imagine if you were bleeding for twelve long years!
2. Mothers, imagine your little girl continuing to hemorrhage for twelve years!
3. Fathers, imagine if your twelve-year-old daughter started her menstrual cycle, and had to be separated from you for twelve years!
4. Wives, imagine having your monthly period and having to be separated from your husbands and children. Not being able to come home for twelve years, watching your husband and children from afar?
5. Husbands, imagine your wives being sick and separated from you for twelve years but you aren't able to visit, stroke their hair, hold their hands or hug her!

This Certain Woman had suffered many things of many physicians:

1. They used her as a guinea pig
2. They tested their different medicines on her
3. They allowed the medical students to look her over
4. She spent all her money:
5. If she had a lot or a little money, it was spent up

In our time:

1. She would have maxed out on how much her insurance allowed.
2. She would have used up all the credit cards.
3. Taken out as many loans as she could!
4. Used up as much charitable care that she could!
5. The church would have raised as many offering as they could!

But nothing or anyone could help her!!

The money was all gone, and instead of her getting better, she got worse. There are many of you wives who have spent your all emotionally, spiritually, psychologically, financially, trying to save your marriage! You have gone to see your Pastor and every marriage counselor. You have bought and read every book on marriage, but nothing has helped!! Nothing or no one can make your husband be the husband that he vowed to be.

What do you do when you have gone to see all the marriage counselors in town, and none of them can get your husband to do right by you? What do you do when you have done all that you can do? What do you do when you have an issue that money cannot fix? Your Pastor, can't get your husband to do, right?

What do you do when mama, daddy, family, friend, cannot help you? What do you do when you have exhausted all of your resources, and you have done all that you could do to "get" your husband to be that husband that he said he would be? But instead, he has caused many issues for you? What do you do after 20 years of marriage he has not changed but is still cheating on you? Because the truth is, you can only "change" you!! You cannot cause your husband to do right by you! That is a decision he must make and live daily!!

What is your issue?

What is it that ails you, my dear?
1. Abuse.
2. Adultery.
3. Abandonment.
4. Sexual abuse of you and your children.
5. Are you praying that God would change your husband?
6. Are you in a sexless marriage.
7. Were you deceived?
8. Was your choice to choose stolen from you?
9. Are you married but you are a single woman and mom?
10. Did you trap him by getting pregnant and now you feel trapped?

What is your issue?

1. Do you have a decision that you need to make?
2. Are you in an abusive relationship wondering what people will think if you leave?
3. Are you contemplating divorce or separation?
4. Are you depressed?
5. Did you ignore the red flags and now you feel as if you are being punished?
6. Did you marry him thinking you can change him?
7. Have you come to the end of your rope?
8. Have you exhausted all of your resources?
9. Are you staying in a bad marriage because of the kids or finances?
10. Do you feel as if God has abandoned you?
11. Are you crying, yelling, screaming, and trying to get a word from God about your issue?

This Certain Woman during her pain, hurt, discouragement, weakness, embarrassment, at the end of her rope, she heard about Jesus! See, sometimes you just need a WORD!!

Whose Voice Is on Repeat in Your Mind?

Imagine with me if you will, this Certain Woman trying to get to Jesus. She's weak and weary! She's been bleeding for twelve long years. She is dragging herself, but during her pressing her way, she remembered: **Lev 15:19, And if a woman has an issue, and her issue in her flesh be blood, she shall be put away for seven days: and whosoever touch her shall be unclean until the even.**

How about you? What voice is playing over and over in your head as you are pressing your way to freedom? Whose voice is on repeat in your head? Is it the voice that says "you ain't nothing and won't nobody want you?" Or is it the voice of "you are a purchased possession, and you can do all things through Christ who strengthens you!" Is it the voice that said, "if you leave I'm going to kill you and your kids!" Or is it the voice that says "no weapon formed against you shall prosper!"

Even though this Certain Woman was reminded of the "Law," she did not allow it to stop her. And she knew that there was freedom if she could get to touch Jesus! She made up in her mind that desperate situations, call for drastic measures!

Recently, one of my sisters in the Lord, who attended one of our sister churches was shot dead in front of her kids by her husband, who was an elder. When my spiritual dad, called to informed me, the only question that came to mind was: *"I wonder how many times did she let the church know that she was being abused, but they pushed her to stay and pray?"*

Ladies, let me tell you something my daddy told me! He said:

"IT IS NOT GOD'S WILL FOR YOU TO BE ABUSED BY YOUR HUSBAND OR ANY MAN!"

Sometimes, Sistas, there are some voices in our minds that will keep you bound; even when you know, you need to break free. So, picture this Certain Woman with me. She is squeezing her way through the crowd, but that voice is playing nonstop in her mind. She is on the ground crawling on all fours, trying to get to Jesus. People noticed her desperation and moved away because they knew her situation.

At the same time, the closer she gets to her breakthrough, the lesser the voice of the law becomes. People see her pushing through, but they knew that if she touched them, then they would become unclean. So, they isolated her because they didn't want to become like her.

There are sometimes in your situation that you're not only going to pray and seek God, but you also must get you some help!! People will talk about you, but you know you need to press on for your breakthrough. And you cannot allow what people will say or think about you to hold you bound. This Certain Woman was determined to get to her breakthrough even though people were looking at her and talking about her.

However, she ignored their stares, sneers and their disgust as they turned up their noses. Picture her with me, please!! As she continued to press her way through the crowd, she is stretching to reach Jesus, but the closer she gets, the more Jesus takes another step! Sometimes, it will seem as if when you are about to get your breakthrough; your answer seems to get further and further away.

Talk to Yourself!

As the Certain Woman, presses her way, she continued to make her confession. I can imagine her saying to herself "If I but touch his clothes, I'll be made whole. If I could just get to Jesus, I will be made whole! I just want to touch the hem of his garment!" Can you hear this Certain Woman in your imagination, talking to herself!? You see my Sistas, sometimes; you just have to talk to yourself! Encourage yourself in the Lord!! Remind yourself of the promises of God! Remind yourself that you are unique and you deserve God's very best! Look in your mirror, point to yourself and talk to you!!!

Breakthrough

This Certain Woman continued to stretch and press her way, still confessing, "If I touch him I'll be made whole!" And the closer she gets to Jesus, the more steps he took.

But, all of a sudden, she caught up to him and touched his clothes! Right away, the fountain of her blood was dried up. Suddenly, something happened inside of her. Something was different; she felt that she was healed of that plague. Verse 30 says, Jesus immediately knowing in himself, that virtue had gone out of him, turned Him about in the crowd, and said: *"who touched me?"*

Jesus, the son of the living God, asked this Certain Woman a question!! Think about this! When God asks a question, it's not necessarily for you to answer him, but it's for you to stop and take notice.

What Question Has God Asked You?

Like this Certain Woman, have you made up in your mind that you need an answer from God about your situation? Jesus was about to make an example out of this Certain Woman, as He did with the saints in **Hebrews**

11. Jesus wanted this Certain Woman to make a public declaration of what God had done for her. So, Jesus asked: *"who touched me?"*

There are some things that mama, daddy, aunty, uncle, pastor or the marriage counselor can't fix!! There are some things that only Jesus can fix!! I am all for going to the doctor, see a counselor and everything else. But sometimes, there are some heart and soul issues that only Jesus and His Word can fix. When this Certain Woman, touched Jesus, something happened to Him and her. She connected with Him in faith, and Jesus was not made unclean because the power in Him dispelled the presence of death and defilement in her.

What are your issues that you need to go sit down and have a little talk with Jesus about? What are you going through that you have talked to everyone else about, but you have yet to go and talk to your father about? This Certain Woman, fearing and trembling, knowing what was done in her came and fell before Jesus and told him all the truth. Sometimes, God just wants us to come to him baring it all and being honest with him. Tell Him, who hurt you and where it hurts. Tell Him how He is the only one that can fix your heart, soul, and your spirit issue!!

Daughter!

Notice Jesus' words to her! He didn't address her as a Certain Woman, but he spoke to her true identity and said **'DAUGHTER!'** Jesus calling her **DAUGHTER** restored her to her rightful place in Him.

And so, I call you **DAUGHTER**! In spite of what you have been through, you're not that! You are not the divorce, the abuse, the infidelities, or anything else that was done to you to try and destroy who you are as **DAUGHTER OF THE KING**!!

Jesus said "…your faith has made you whole:" See, when you go to Christ, He knows what you need. And he is a God of overflow! So you might go to God about issue "A," but God will heal issues "A to Z." Jesus spoke to all of who she was and to her brokenness. Jesus said your faith has made you WHOLE!!

DAUGHTER OF THE KING, I submit to you that Jesus wants to make you whole. It was not his will that you went through what you went through. God created marriage as a picture of the marriage between Christ and the Church. Jesus loves the church so much that He died for her.

Your husband was to love you like Christ loves the Church. Christ would never cheat, abuse, rape, abandon, mistreat the church or any other of the negative and bad things that were done to you. Christ's will, when He brought Eve to Adam was for Adam to profess his love, provide for and protect her, even if his life depended on it!

Honestly, I do believe that very few couples experience and enjoy the Christ and Church type of marriage. Another thing I want to point out is that the enemy hates marriage. That is why the institution of marriage has come under such attack. Additionally, the enemy knows that if he gets the head, then the body will follow.

Unfortunately, you cannot have a marriage all alone, because God created marriage to be between one man and one woman. Therefore, it requires both people to participate. Once the enemy gets the head, he plans to destroy the rest of the body which is the wife and children. But, I thank God that he wants you to know that **Jesus has made you whole!!**

Be Made Whole

As Jesus spoke wholeness to his Daughter, I speak those same words to you today as you read this book.

Be Whole in every area of your life:

a. Physically
b. Spiritually
c. Emotionally
d. Socially
e. Financially
f. Psychologically

Jesus wants you to be whole in your whole being:

1. **Spirit**: The part of you that can relate to God and which comes alive when you accepted Christ.
2. **Soul**: Houses your will, intellect and your emotions.
3. **Body**: Is your earth suit in the earth.

You can read more about this in my book *Daughters of the King*, coming soon.

Jesus instructed the once known Certain Woman, now Daughter, to **"...go in peace, and be whole of thy plague."** Guess what? Jesus is speaking those same words to you today. Whatever your issue is, God wants you to touch Him, and in return, He will touch you and dry up that issue in your life today.

Jesus wants you to be whole in your soul which is made up of your will, intellect, and emotions. When you begin to be whole, you need to forgive those that have hurt you, those who talked about you, those who laughed and scorned you when you were struggling with your issue.

Jesus wants you to be WHOLE TODAY!! You cannot be the whole begging, crying, nagging, speaking negatively, and so on. But you can be whole by Faith and faith alone!

Faith?

What is Faith? **Hebrews 11:1 Now faith is the substance of things hoped for, the evidence of things not seen.** The first thing about faith is that it is NOW! It is present, today, at this very moment. Faith is not tomorrow, next week or next year. Faith is not going to do or come, but faith is NOW!!

Another critical truth about faith is that it's ACTIVE!! Faith just doesn't sit down and do nothing, it gets up and acts!

Let's define a few words in **Hebrew 11**:

1. Now (What does 'now' mean to you?)
2. The substance is something that is physical.
3. Things hoped for: hoping for something.
4. Evidence: proof.
5. The last phrase is 'not seen": you cannot see it, or that it is invisible to you.

When you put it all together, what it means is that FAITH is NOW, and it is the physical thing that you are hoping for. In other words, your faith is the proof that you have what you do not see with your physical eyes yet.

Remember, faith is always NOW, not yesterday or tomorrow, but right now. Whatever you believe God for, God has already given it to you. And all you need to do is to receive it in Jesus' name.

Faith speaks what God speaks, thinks what God thinks, and believes what God believes. God thinks, believes, and says that you are healed now, today, at this very moment, because faith is NOW!

Putting It All Together

So, are you wondering why I'm sharing the story of this Certain Woman along with Faith? I'm glad you asked. Read on!!

Remember the woman with the issue of blood? What did she say? She said, "If I touch him, then I will be healed." But, she needed to touch him to receive healing because SHE HAD AN ISSUE OF BLOOD!! As I asked earlier, what is your issue? Whatever your issue is, it has caused you to be broken, sadden, hurt, disappointed, angry and bitter.

My Sistas which shared their stories with me realized that they are *THE NAKED WIFE*!! You might be reading *The Naked Wife* because this book title has spoken to and you recognize that you too are *The Naked Wife*.

However, like the Certain Woman with the issue of blood, Jesus wants to make you whole and restore you to your rightful place of DAUGHTER, COVERED and WHOLE! (Please see my Covered and Whole Journal) But for you to get there, you need to admit that you have an issue.

Once you have admitted that you have an issue, be it resentment, bitterness, anger, hurt or disappointments. You might even have a black eye, some broken bones, and bruises all over your body, by the man who vowed to protect you.

If you are physically abused, I URGE YOU TO CALL 911 NOW!!

Look in the mirror and tell yourself that you have an issue and you need to get some help! God is a God of faith, but faith is now and active. So if you are in an abusive marriage, honey you need to pray, but while you pray, you need to pack also!

Maybe your issue is fear? Whatever it is, you need to address it head on!! Until you face your issue head-on, God cannot do His part. God needs

271

permission to move in your life. Permit him by making your declaration of faith like the woman with the issue of blood.

When your marriage as God intended it to fell apart, your whole world fell. When you began reading *The Naked Wife,* you were NAKED!! But I declare that you are no longer NAKED WIVES!!

Naked No More!!

But, I call you DAUGHTERS OF THE KING, WHOLE and COVERED IN JESUS NAME!!! {Please see my *Daughters of the King,* book as a follow up to *The Naked Wife.*}

I speak healing to that:

- hurt
- pain
- resentment
- bitterness
- disappointment
- and your brokenness!

I speak wholeness to your:

Body: Many of you were physically abused by your husbands that were to protect you. But for every:

- time the man that was supposed to protect you but abused you instead, I speak healing!!
- bruise that he caused, I speak healing.
- broken bone, I call you healed in Jesus name!!
- wife that was raped by your husband, I call you whole, covered and healed!

Soul; your intellect, will, and emotions.

- For every time you were called stupid, I call you wise and smart!
- When your voice or opinion didn't matter, I declare that someone wants to hear your story. Perhaps your voice is the voice they need to step out on faith!
- For every pain that was caused emotionally, God is the breasted one. Lay on God your father's heart and tell him all about it.

272

- Allow him to heal your heart. I called you heal, right now in Jesus name!!

Spirit: Your spirit is the part of you that is most like God.

- For every time your spirit was broken, I breathe the breath of life and the Word of God back into you right now!!
- For every time, he killed your spirit; I command your spirit to come alive in Jesus name!

I CALL YOU HEALED, WHOLE AND COVERED, IN JESUS NAME!!

Your Part

Finally, here is your part! I believe each person should fight for their marriage. I also believe that it takes both people working together at the marriage to make it work. But I also believe that after you have done all that you can do, then you stand on God's Word according to **Ephesians 6**.

Take the following steps:

1.   You recognized that at one time you were naked, but as of a few moments ago, you are no longer NAKED. Instead of being NAKED you are now COVERED and WHOLE.

2.   Allow the Holy Spirit to minister to you.

3.   Give your husband or ex-husband to God and allow the Lord to have His way.

4.   Pray for your husband or ex-husband that caused your nakedness and brokenness.

5.   Forgive him. Well, that's easier said than done you might be saying! I agree with you, so you forgive him in faith! Take it one day at a time.

6. Don't think about tomorrow or next year, just forgive him today. And when tomorrow comes, forgive him tomorrow. One day at a time.

7.   Do not ask God to change your husband anymore. Disappointments creep in when you have been asking for something, and it doesn't happen.

8. Instead, daily speak what you would like to experience in your life. Death and life are in the power of your tongue, and you will have what you say.

9. Do not ask God to help your husband to cover you. If he is not in the place to do so, you will only end up right where you were before.

10. If you have not sought counseling for your marriage and both of you would like to save your marriage, then I encourage you to do so.

11. I believe that couples should have continual counseling. My husband and I go to counseling a few times per year. We get our cars checked, get a physical, get a cleaning at the dentist, why not have a marital checkup?

12. It doesn't mean something is wrong, but I am reminded of the scriptures that say it's the little foxes that spoil the vine.

13. Ask your husband to read this book and have some open and honest conversations.

Prayer

Father, in Jesus name, I thank you that I am no longer a naked wife, but I am a covered, whole and healed daughter of the King.

Lord, I open up my heart, mind, soul, and body to you for you to have your way and minister to me in Jesus name.

Holy Spirit breath through me and manifest your healing in Jesus name.

I forgive those that have caused the nakedness in my life. Thank you that you have covered me in Jesus name.

Father, from this day forward, I walk in my covering, wholeness, and healing in Jesus name.

Prayer of Salvation

If you have read this book and you have not accepted Jesus, I encourage you to do so.

According to **Romans 10:9, if you confess with your mouth the Lord Jesus Christ, and believe in your heart that God raised from the dead, you shall be saved.**

Pray the following:

I confess with my mouth, the Lord Jesus Christ, and I believe in my heart that God has raised you from the dead and now I am saved.

Jesus, I invite you to come into my heart and save me. Come into my heart and live with me forever. Thank you, Lord, for saving me.

WELCOME TO THE BODY OF CHRIST!!

Simple isn't it!?

Thank you for reading The Naked Wife. I pray that your life was changed for the better. Remember that we are sisters saving sisters.

Blessings and Love
Janice

JANICE HYLTON-THOMPSON

About the Author

*J*anice is the wife of her wonderful husband Michael Sr, and mom of two excellent children born 20 years apart. Janice's beautiful and fashionable daughter, Alexia, and her inquisitive and joyful son, Michael Jr.

Janice loves and treasures her family and enjoys spending time with them, making their favorite meals, watching movies and enjoying a day at the park. Shopping and doing girl's stuff with Alexia, and playing on the floor with her 2-year-old son, Michael Jr, who she is still nursing.

Janice loves to read and write and writes passionately about subjects that mean the most to her. Additionally, Janice loves to tackle those "rock the boat" subjects as a blogger and author.

Janice's motto is "Teaching & Writing in Simplicity; That Even A Child Will Understand. Janice's teaching ministry is under the covering of her spiritual father, Bishop Marvin Bradshaw Sr.

Janice is the author of several books and has been writing for over 20 years. Her published books include:

1. Praying for Our Children
2. In Christ I Am
3. In Christ, I Am Prayer Journal
4. In Christ, I Am Bible Study Journal
5. Moments of Gratitude
6. The Phenomenon of Donald J Trump – The GOP Nominee
7. The Naked Wife

Coming Soon

8. Covered and Whole Journal – The Companion to The Naked Wife
9. Profess, Provide & Protect Journal – From The Naked Wife Series

10. Daughters of The King: A Follow Up to The Naked Wife
11. Sacrifice of Marriage
12. Singles.

Also, Janice blogs @

Janice Hylton Blog @ www.janicehyltonblog.com where she encourages and empower women to walk in their royalty as daughters of the King.

Mommy 20 Years Apart @ www.mommy20yearsapart.com where she blogs about adjusting to motherhood in two different worlds.

If you would like to connect with Janice online, you can do so on:

Facebook

Author Janice Hylton-Thompson https://www.facebook.com/Author-Janice-Hylton-Thompson-273058339571807/

Janice Hylton Blog @ https://www.facebook.com/Janice-Hylton-Blog-328934510397/

Praying For Our Children @ https://www.facebook.com/Praying-For-Our-Children-177006725710062/

Mommy 20 Years Apart @ https://www.facebook.com/Mommy-20-Years-Apart-1085441701601831/

Twitter

The Janice Hylton @ https://twitter.com/Thejanicehylton
Janice Hylton Blog @ https://twitter.com/janiceblog

Pinterest

https://www.pinterest.ca/janicehyltonblog/

Thank You

My Team: To my editors, formatters, and cover designers. We have worked on quite a few projects, and I am so grateful for all of your help.

Sherry Kaye Chamblee @ www.offscript.weebly.com, you have worked with me on several projects, and I feel so blessed and honored to have you in my life. Thank you for always being available to answer questions and do quick reviews for me.

Neil D'Silva @ Pen, Paper Coffee, brother I am so grateful for you. This is the second project we have worked on, and I am grateful for all of your help and advice and quick edits. Thank you for always being available to answer quick questions and help.

Rebecca @ Rebecca Covers: You are a Godsend!!! I had several covers made, but no one was able to capture my vision like you did. And for that, I will forever be grateful. You have created several covers for me and revised some that were already done, and with every cover, I just love and appreciate you more. You are a brilliant designer, and I pray that your gift will make room for you.

Dorothy @ www.dorothydreyer.com: You are a Godsend! Four formatters bailed on me but then God allowed us to meet. Thank you so much and I wish you many successes. Blessings.

Fellow Authors: You know who you are, always available to help and answer quick questions, give advice and tips. Thank you!!

Made in the USA
Coppell, TX
10 March 2022

74770639R00171